MW01011685

A PRACTICAL FIELD GUIDE
FOR ISO 14001:2015

Also by Erik V. Myhrberg:

The ISO 9001:2015 QMS "Bluesheet" ©2015

The ISO 14001:2015 EMS "Greensheet" ©2015

The OHSAS 18001:2007 HSMS "Redsheet" ©2007

The ISO 27001:2013 ISMS "Goldsheet" ©2013

Also available from ASQ Quality Press:

A Practical Field Guide for ISO 9001:2015
Erik V. Myhrberg

A Practical Field Guide for ISO 13485
Erik V. Myhrberg

The ISO 14001:2015 Implementation Handbook: Using the Process Approach to Build an Environmental Management System
Milton P. Dentch

ISO Lesson Guide 2015: Pocket Guide to ISO 9001:2015, Fourth Edition
J.P. Russell

How to Audit ISO 9001:2015: A Handbook for Auditors
Chad Kymal

How to Establish a Document Control System for Compliance with ISO 9001:2015, ISO 13485:2016, and FDA Requirements: A Comprehensive Guide to Designing a Process-Based Document Control System
Stephanie L. Skipper

ISO 9001:2015 Explained, Fourth Edition
Charles A. Cianfrani and John E. "Jack" West

ISO 9001:2015 Internal Audits Made Easy, Fourth Edition
Ann W. Phillips

ISO 9001:2015 for Small and Medium-Sized Businesses, Third Edition
Denise Robitaille

The Certified Quality Engineer Handbook, Fourth Edition
Sarah E. Burke and Rachel T. Silvestrini

Root Cause Analysis: Simplified Tools and Techniques, Second Edition
Bjørn Andersen and Tom Fagerhaug

The Certified Manager of Quality/Organizational Excellence Handbook, Third Edition
Russell T. Westcott, editor

To request a complimentary catalog of ASQ Quality Press publications, call 800-248-1946, or visit our website at http://www.asq.org/quality-press.

A PRACTICAL FIELD GUIDE
FOR ISO 14001:2015

- Leadership Guidance

- Revision and Update Information

- Implementation Support

- Documented Information

- Internal Auditing Technique

- Risks and Opportunities

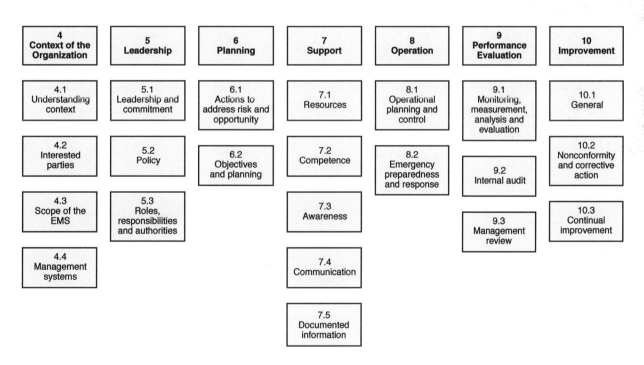

Erik V. Myhrberg with Brandon L. Myhrberg

ASQ Quality Press
Milwaukee, Wisconsin

American Society for Quality, Quality Press, Milwaukee 53203
© 2018 by ASQ. Published 2017.
All rights reserved.
Printed in the United States of America
23 22 21 20 19 18   5 4 3 2 1

Library of Congress Cataloging-in-Publication Data
Names: Myhrberg, Erik V., author. | Myhrberg, Brandon L., author.
Title: A practical field guide for ISO 14001:2015 : leadership guidance,
   revision and update information, implementation support, documented
   information, internal auditing technique, risks and opportunities / Dr.
   Erik V. Myhrberg with Brandon L. Myhrberg.
Description: Milwaukee, Wisconsin : ASQ Quality Press, [2017]
Identifiers: LCCN 2017034376 | ISBN 9780873899635 (pbk. : alk. paper)
Subjects: LCSH: ISO 14001 Standard. | Factory and trade waste—Standards. |
   Environmental protection—Standards. | Business enterprises—Environmental
   aspects—Standards. | Operations research—Standards.
Classification: LCC TD897.5 .M94 2017 | DDC 628.5/10218—dc23
LC record available at https://lccn.loc.gov/2017034376

ISBN: 978-0-87389-963-5

No part of this book may be reproduced in any form or by any means, electronic, mechanical, photocopying, recording, or otherwise, without the prior written permission of the publisher.

Director of Quality Press and Programs: Ray Zielke
Managing Editor: Paul Daniel O'Mara
Sr. Creative Services Specialist: Randy L. Benson

ASQ Mission: The American Society for Quality advances individual, organizational, and community excellence worldwide through learning, quality improvement, and knowledge exchange.

Attention Bookstores, Wholesalers, Schools, and Corporations: ASQ Quality Press books, video, audio, and software are available at quantity discounts with bulk purchases for business, educational, or instructional use. For information, please contact ASQ Quality Press at 800-248-1946, or write to ASQ Quality Press, P.O. Box 3005, Milwaukee, WI 53201–3005.

To place orders or to request a free copy of the ASQ Quality Press Publications Catalog, visit our website at http://www.asq.org/quality-press.

∞ Printed on acid-free paper

Quality Press
600 N. Plankinton Ave.
Milwaukee, WI 53203-2914
E-mail: authors@asq.org
ASQ **The Global Voice of Quality**®

To my blessed family:
Marcena, Brandon, and Heather

To my diligent colleague:
David R.

To my professional associations:
IRCA, IEMA, ASQ

TABLE OF CONTENTS

INTRODUCTION

The ISO 14001:2004 environmental management standard has been revised after more than a decade of use. The ISO 14001:2015 standard has adopted Annex SL of the ISO Directives and will have the same clause structure as the ISO 9001:2015 standard.

More than 25 years have passed (and over 160 projects) since we first became aware of, and started using, the ISO 14001 standard. So much has changed and evolved during this time. These changes include the advent of the ISO 14001 and ISO 27001 management standards, the addition and deletion of standards within the ISO 9000 series, and the creation of a host of industrial and sector-specific standards and "reports" based on ISO 14001, such as AS9100D for aerospace and ISO 13485 for medical devices.

Even with all this progress, the fundamental use of the ISO 14000 series has not changed. Companies, teams, and individuals are still trying to meet customer expectations; worldwide competition still drives the need for innovation; internal process pressures still demand continual improvement in order to remain functional.

This field guide has been created to foster an inner reliance between senior management, middle management, functional teams, and the individual. Users of the field guide will find within it practical tools, tips, and techniques useful for not only implementing an environmental management system (EMS) but also maintaining one.

Per the standard, one of the key purposes of an environmental management system is to act as a preventive tool. Consequently, this International Standard does not have a separate clause or sub-clause on preventive action. The concept of preventive action is expressed through the use of risk-based thinking in formulating environmental management system requirements.

The risk-based thinking applied in this International Standard has enabled some reduction in prescriptive requirements and their replacement by performance-based requirements. There is greater flexibility than in ISO 14001:2004 in the requirements for processes, documented information, and organizational responsibilities.

The revised ISO 14001:2015 standard is both useful to the organization and here to stay. May this logistical field guide serve you and your organization well!

Erik V. Myhrberg

HOW TO USE THIS FIELD GUIDE

The intent of this field guide is to assist organizations, step by step, in implementing an EMS in conformance with ISO 14001:2015, whether "from scratch" or by transitioning from ISO 14001:2004. In keeping with ISO 9000:2015's definition of *environmental* as the "degree to which a set of inherent characteristics fulfills requirements," I have identified the requirements and inherent characteristics (distinguishing features) for this field guide. Within the guide, each sub-clause containing requirements is the focus of a two-page spread that consistently presents features that fulfill the requirements listed below.

Requirements (Or What the Field Guide Will Do)

- Provide a user-friendly guide to ISO 14001:2015's requirements for implementation purposes.

- Identify the documents/documentation required, along with recommendations on what to consider retaining/adding to an EMS during ISO 14001:2015 implementation.

- Guide internal auditor(s) regarding what to ask to verify that a conforming and effective EMS exists.

- Direct management on what it must do and should consider to satisfy ISO 14001:2015's enhanced requirements and responsibilities for top management.

- Depict step by step what must occur to create an effective, conforming EMS.

INHERENT CHARACTERISTICS
(OR WHAT THE FIELD GUIDE PROVIDES)

- *Standard*—A heads-up of what a sub-clause of ISO 14001:2015 requires in easy-to-understand language, with references to information in ISO 9000:2015 and guidance in ISO 9004:2016(CD) to enhance the user's understanding of what ISO 14001:2015 requires and what possible added steps the user can take to improve performance.

- *Documentation*—A list of the documented information required by the sub-clause, with some ideas to consider in satisfying those requirements that will take the system beyond the requirements toward continual improvement.

- *Internal audit questions*—What every internal audit team needs to ask at a minimum when assessing the EMS for conformance with the sub-clause.

- *Management*—A brief description of what management must do and/or is responsible for in order to achieve conformance to the sub-clause, along with some guidance on additional steps management can take to enhance the system.

- *Flowcharts*—A depiction of the steps that need to be undertaken during an implementation/transition effort to effectively and efficiently satisfy the requirements of the sub-clause of ISO 14001:2015, along with a box providing guidance on use of the flowchart.

- *Correlation*—A matrix that shows where the requirements in each sub-clause within a section of ISO 14001:2004 appear in ISO 14001:2015.

- These cross-evaluations are provided to assist those users whose organizations are transitioning from ISO 14001:2004 and appear at the end of the field guide's coverage of each clause of ISO 14001:2015 (clauses 4–10).

This field guide is designed to provide you with a consistent approach to implementing an ISO 14001:2015–conforming EMS, which is appropriate since ISO 14001:2015 continues to view environmental as the ability of an organization to consistently deliver product that meets customer specifications. The field guide examines each sub-clause of clauses 4–10 of ISO 14001:2015, which contain the requirements, with characteristics 1–4 presented on the even page and characteristic 5 presented on the facing odd page.

The new standard adopts the format and terminology of Annex SL. Annex SL was developed to ensure all future ISO management system standards would share a common format, irrespective of the specific discipline to which they relate. Annex SL prescribes a high-level structure, identical core text, and common terms and definitions. This means that even when requirements are essentially unchanged between ISO 14001:2004 and ISO 14001:2015, these are frequently found under a new clause/sub-clause heading.

Per ISO 14001:2015:

Where ISO 14001:2004 used specific terminology such as "document" or "documented procedures," "environmental manual" or "environmental plan," this edition of this International Standard defines requirements to "maintain documented information."

Where ISO 14001:2004 used the term "records" to denote documents needed to provide evidence of conformity with requirements, this is now expressed as a requirement to "retain documented information." The organization is responsible for determining what documented information needs to be retained, the period of time for which it is to be retained, and the media to be used for its retention.

A requirement to "maintain" documented information does not exclude the possibility that the organization might also need to "retain" that same documented information for a particular purpose, e.g., to retain previous versions of it.

What separates this field guide from most other books on ISO 14001:2015 and its implementation are the flowcharts showing the steps to be taken in implementing an EMS to meet a sub-clause's requirements. But the flowcharts themselves can be overwhelming when you first look at them. For this reason, a box appears with each flowchart that explains pertinent facts and/or what the flowchart represents and how it is to be used.

Remember, the EMS your organization implements must meet the needs of its users—you and the rest of your organization's employees, from senior management to the most junior employee. So the EMS you create using this field guide will not only satisfy ISO 14001:2015's requirements, but will provide a set of processes that suits your organization and will foster improved use of the system and improvement in the processes of the organization as it matures.

ANNEX SL

Annex SL addresses the requirements for all management system standards.

It consists of nine clauses and three appendices, and the audience for this annex is primarily ISO technical committees who develop management system standards. However, all users of management system standards will feel the impact of Appendix 2 of Annex SL.

There are three sections:

- High-level structure (HLS)

- Identical core text (core)

- Common terms and core definitions (T&D)

All management system standards will need to have these clauses. There will be less confusion and inconsistency as all common terms will have the same definition, and there will be common requirements across all management system standards—for example, the requirement to establish, implement, maintain, and improve continually the management system.

There is a high-level structure. The major clause numbers and titles of all management system standards will be identical. They are:

Introduction

1. Scope

2. Normative references

3. Terms and definitions

4. Context of the organization

5. Leadership

6. Planning

7. Support

8. Operation

9. Performance evaluation

10. Improvement

The introduction, scope, and normative references will have content that are specific to each discipline and each standard can have its own bibliography.

All management system standards have these same 10 high-level clauses.

CLAUSE 4: CONTEXT OF THE ORGANIZATION

4.1 Understanding the organization and its context
4.2 Understanding the needs and expectations of interested parties
4.3 Determining the scope of the environmental management system
4.4 Environmental management system

Overview: The organization needs to determine and document its own scope—where are the boundaries of the management system? What's in and what's out? The scope must be appropriate to the organization and its objectives, and the organization also needs to build, operate, and improve its management system. The issues and requirements identified here will be carried forward as considerations into clause 6—Planning.

The Standard: 4.0 Context of the Organization

4.1 Understanding the organization and its context

The standard requires organizations to identify, monitor, and review internal and external issues that are relevant to its purpose and strategic direction, and that could impact the environmental management system's intended results.

Documented Information:

Required:

None

Cross-Reference 2004:

New requirement

Internal Audit Questions:	*Management:*
Internal auditors may ask:	Changes:
• Has the organization determined its external and internal issues (those relevant to its purpose and that affect its ability to achieve the intended outcomes of its environmental management system)?	• This is a new requirement on the context of the organization.
• Are environmental conditions affected by, or capable of affecting, the organization included as issues?	• The Notes provide examples of contextual issues.
	• Your organization may already monitor and review these issues.
	• Auditors will look for evidence of issue monitoring and reviews.

ISO 14001:2015—Section 4.1
Understanding the organization and its context

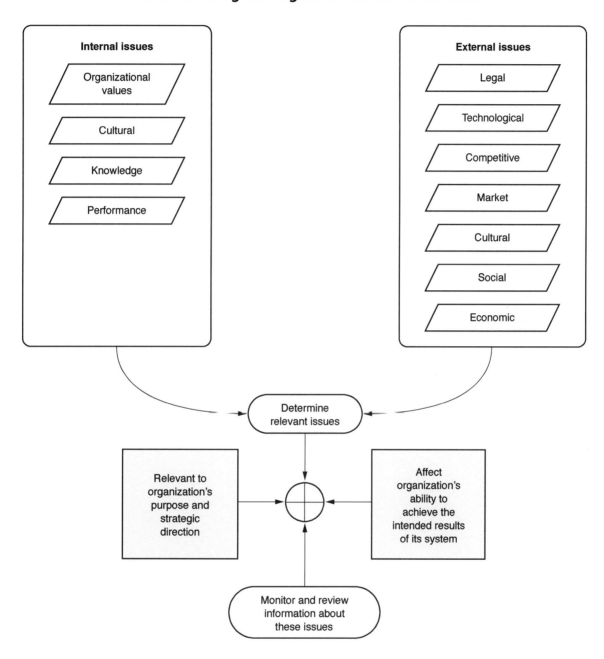

Changes from ISO 14001:2004:

• This is a new requirement on the context of the organization.

• The Notes provide examples of external and internal issues.

• Your organization may already monitor and review these issues.

• Auditors will look for evidence of issue monitoring and reviews.

The Standard: 4.0 Context of the Organization

4.2 Understanding the needs and expectations of interested parties

The organization is required to determine "the relevant requirements" of "relevant interested parties."

Once determined, the organization must then monitor and review the information it holds about these parties and their requirements.

Documented Information:

Required:

None

Cross-Reference 2004:

New requirement

Internal Audit Questions:	Management:

Internal auditors may ask:
 	
• Has the organization determined:
 	
  a) The interested parties that are relevant to the EMS?
 	
  b) The relevant needs and expectations (i.e., requirements) of these interested parties?
 	
  c) Which of these needs and expectations become its compliance obligations?
	Changes:
	
	• This is a new requirement on interested parties.
	
	• The relevant interested parties may change.
	
	• The relevant requirements may also change.
	
	• Auditors will need evidence of periodic reviews.

ISO 14001:2015—Section 4.2
Understanding the needs and expectations of interested parties

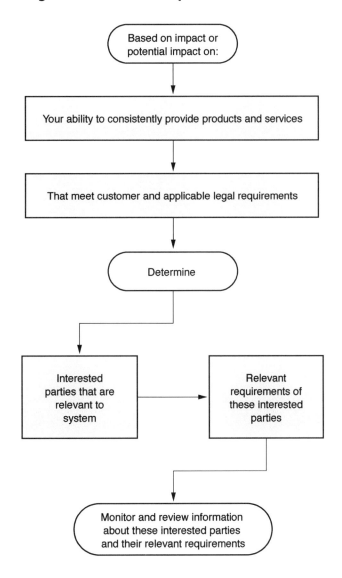

Changes from ISO 14001:2004:

• This is a new requirement on interested parties.

• The relevant interested parties may change.

• The relevant requirements may also change.

• Auditors will need evidence of periodic reviews.

The Standard: 4.0 Context of the Organization

4.3 Determining the scope of the environmental management system

When defining the scope of its environmental management system, the organization needs to take into account its context (e.g., the internal and external issues it faces and the requirements of relevant interested parties) and also the products and/or services it intends to deliver.

The scope must be made available and be maintained as documented information.

Documented Information:

Required:

4.3—Scope statement

Cross-Reference 2004:

1.2 Application

4.1 General requirements

Internal Audit Questions:	*Management:*
Internal auditors may ask:	Changes:
• Has the organization determined the boundaries and applicability of the EMS to establish its scope?	• This clause 4.3 replaces the need for old clause 1.2, Application.
• Has the organization considered when determining the scope:	• Specifying the scope of the system is not a new requirement.
a) External and internal issues referred to in 4.1?	• Adds the requirement to consider issues, interested parties, and products and services.
b) Compliance obligations referred to in 4.2?	• Exclusions are no longer limited to old clause 7, Product Realization.
c) Organizational units, functions, and physical boundaries?	• See the new Annex A.5 for more on the applicability of requirements.
d) Activities, products, and services?	
e) Authority and ability to exercise control and influence?	

ISO 14001:2015—Section 4.3
Determining the scope of the environmental management system

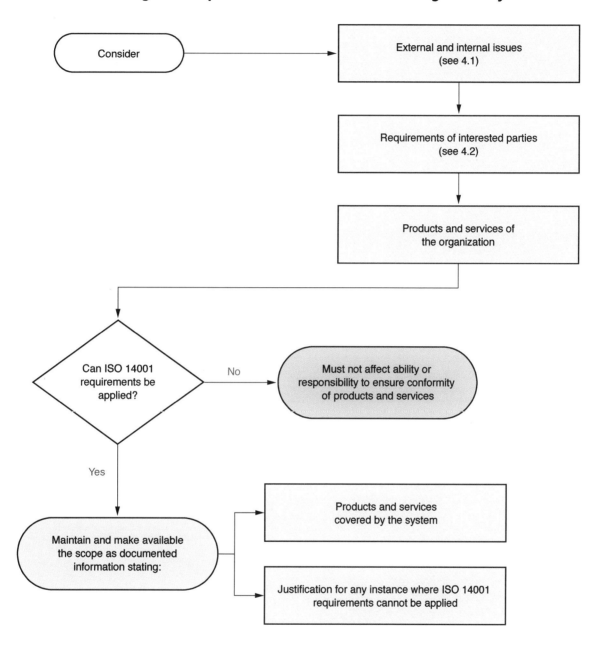

Changes from ISO 14001:2004:

• This clause 4.3 replaces the need for old clause 1.2, Application.

• Specifying the scope of the system is not a new requirement.

• Adds the requirement to consider issues, interested parties, and products and services.

• Exclusions are no longer limited to old clause 7, Product Realization.

• See the new Annex A.5 for more on the applicability of requirements.

The Standard: 4.0 Context of the Organization

4.4 Environmental management system

The standard requires the organization to establish a process-based environmental management system.

Once in place this needs to be maintained and continually improved. Clause 4.4 sets out high-level requirements for the design of a process-based management system.

Documented Information:

Required:

None (but many organizations use a manual here)

Cross-Reference 2004:

4.1 General requirements

Internal Audit Questions:	Management:
Internal auditors may ask:	Changes:
• To achieve intended outcomes, including environmental performance, has organization established, implemented, maintained, and continually improved EMS, including needed processes and their interactions, in accordance with requirements of ISO 14001:2015?	• This clause replaces old clause 4.1 on general process-based requirements.
• Has the organization considered the knowledge gained in 4.1 and 4.2 when establishing and maintaining the EMS?	• Must determine and address process-related risks and opportunities.
	• New focus is on performance indicators for effective operation and control.
	• Discussion of outsourcing in old clause 4.1 was moved to clause 8.1.

ISO 14001:2015—Section 4.4
Environmental management system and its processes

Environmental management system

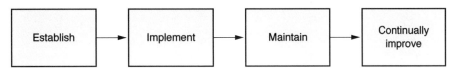

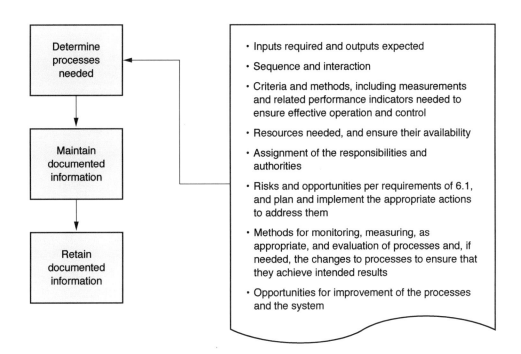

- Inputs required and outputs expected

- Sequence and interaction

- Criteria and methods, including measurements and related performance indicators needed to ensure effective operation and control

- Resources needed, and ensure their availability

- Assignment of the responsibilities and authorities

- Risks and opportunities per requirements of 6.1, and plan and implement the appropriate actions to address them

- Methods for monitoring, measuring, as appropriate, and evaluation of processes and, if needed, the changes to processes to ensure that they achieve intended results

- Opportunities for improvement of the processes and the system

Changes from ISO 14001:2004:

- This clause replaces old clause 4.1 on general process-based requirements.

- Must determine and address process-related risks and opportunities.

- New focus on performance indicators for effective operation and control.

- Discussion of outsourcing in old clause 4.1 was moved to clause 8.1.

UPDATES TO ISO 14001:2004 IN ISO 14001:2015

(Source: L. Whittington)

4. Context of the Organization

4.1 Understanding the Organization and Its Context

ISO 14001:2015 adds to the common Annex SL text that the issues to be determined include environmental conditions that are capable of affecting or being affected by the organization. According to Annex A of ISO 14001:2015, these conditions may include climate, air quality, water quality, land use, existing contamination, natural resource availability, and biodiversity.

4.2 Understanding the Needs and Expectations of Interested Parties

The 14001:2015 standard adds that the organization must determine which of the needs and expectations of the interested parties become compliance obligations. According to its definition, "compliance obligation" is a requirement that an organization has to, or chooses to, comply with.

Obligations may arise from mandatory requirements, such as applicable laws and regulations, or voluntary commitments, such as organization and industry standards, contractual relationships, principles of good governance, and community and ethical standards.

4.3 Determining the Scope of the Environmental Management System

When determining the scope, ISO 14001:2015 adds other issues to be considered: the organization's units, functions, and physical boundaries; its activities, products, and services; and its authority and ability to exercise control and influence. Any activities, products, and services that can have significant environmental aspects must be included in the scope of the environmental management system.

4.4 Environmental Management System

ISO 14001:2015 adds to the Annex SL text that the requirements of the standard are to be met to enhance the environmental performance of the organization.

CLAUSE 5: LEADERSHIP

5.1 Leadership and commitment
5.2 Environmental policy
5.3 Organizational roles, responsibilities and authorities

Overview: There is now a clear emphasis on leadership, not management, and these are not one and the same but very different things. On further examination, it becomes clear that this clause has potentially the most far-reaching implications of any of the Annex SL–induced changes. Top management, those at the highest level in the organization, now have to demonstrate much greater involvement in the operation of the organization's management system.

The Standard: 5.0 Leadership

5.1 Leadership and commitment

Top management must stress the importance of effective environmental management and of conforming to the requirements of the environmental management system.

It must make sure that the environmental management system is achieving the results intended and must lead people to contribute to the effective operation of the system.

Top management must drive continual improvement and innovation, and develop leadership in its managers.

Documented Information:

Required:

None

Cross-Reference 2004:

New requirement

Internal Audit Questions:	Management:
Internal auditors may ask:	Changes:
• Does top management demonstrate leadership and commitment to the EMS by:	• This clause updates old clause 5.1 on management commitment.
a) Taking accountability for the effectiveness of the EMS?	• Determining legal requirements included from old clause 7.2.1.
b) Ensuring that the environmental policy and environmental objectives are established for the EMS and are compatible with the strategic direction and context of organization?	• Primary clauses for customer requirements are new 4.2 and 7.4.3.
c) Ensuring integration of EMS requirements into the organization's business processes?	• Adds the requirement to determine and address risks.
d) Ensuring that the resources needed for the EMS are available?	

ISO 14001:2015—Section 5.1
Leadership and commitment

Demonstrate leadership and commitment to the environmental management system

Accountability for effectiveness	Ensure integration	Ensure resources are available
Engage, direct, and support	Ensure environmental policy and environmental objectives	Promote awareness
Communicate importance of conformance	Promote continual improvement	Environmental policy communicated, understood, and applied
Ensure system achieves intended results	Support other management roles, demonstrate leadership	

Changes from ISO 14001:2004:

• This clause updates old clause 5.1 on management commitment.

• New requirements to demonstrate leadership and accountability.

• Adds that policy and objectives must be compatible with strategic direction.

• Environmental policy must be applied, not just communicated and understood.

• System requirements must now be integrated into business processes.

• Notice the "ensure" requirements that someone else can do, versus "take," "promote," "communicate," "engage," and "support."

• More of a hands-on role for top management.

The Standard: 5.0 Leadership

5.2 Environmental policy

Top management must establish an environmental policy that is consistent with the purpose and context of the organization. It must additionally provide a framework for the setting and review of environmental objectives, and include commitments to satisfy any applicable requirements and to continually improve their environmental management system.

It is the responsibility of top management to review and maintain the environmental policy.

Documented Information:

Required:

5.2—Environmental policy statement

Cross-Reference 2004:

4.2 Environmental policy

Internal Audit Questions:	Management:
Internal auditors may ask:	Changes:

• Has top management established, implemented, and maintained an environmental policy that, within the defined scope of its EMS:
 	
  a) Is appropriate to the purpose and context of the organization, including the nature, scale, and environmental impacts of its activities, products, and services?
 	
  b) Provides a framework for setting environmental objectives?
	• This clause replaces old clause 4.2 on environmental policy.
	
	• Policy must be maintained, not just established and reviewed.
	
	• Policy must be applied, not just communicated and understood.
	
	• Must make policy available to interested parties, as appropriate.

ISO 14001:2015—Section 5.2
Environmental policy

5.2.1 Establishing the environmental policy

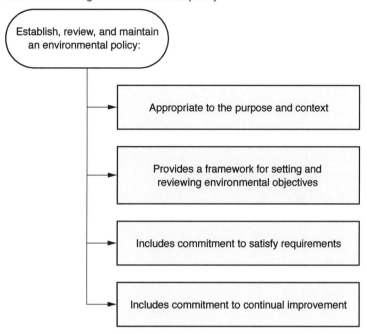

5.2.2 Communicating the environmental policy

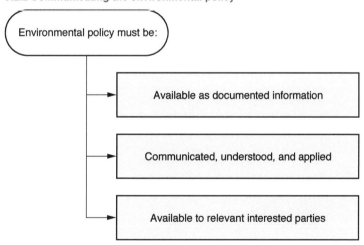

Changes from ISO 14001:2004:

• This clause replaces old clause 4.2 on environmental policy.

• Policy must be maintained, not just established and reviewed.

• Policy must be applied, not just communicated and understood.

• Must make it available to interested parties, as appropriate.

The Standard: 5.0 Leadership

5.3 Organizational roles, responsibilities and authorities

Top management of the organization need to ensure assignment of the necessary responsibilities and authorities to individuals within the organization to carry out environmental-related activities.

Top management need to ensure that responsibilities and authorities relating to an organization's environmental management system are communicated within the organization and that they are understood within the organization.

Documented Information:

Required:

None

Cross-Reference 2004:

4.4.1 Resources, roles, responsibility and authority

Internal Audit Questions:	Management:
Internal auditors may ask:	Changes:
• Does top management ensure that the responsibilities and authorities for relevant roles are assigned and communicated within the organization?	• This clause replaces old clause 4.4.1 on responsibility and authority.
• Has top management assigned the responsibility and authority for:	• Adds that responsibilities must be assigned and understood.
a) Ensuring that the EMS conforms to the requirements of ISO 14001:2015?	• Identifies some specific responsibilities to be assigned.
b) Reporting on the performance of the EMS, including environmental performance, to top management?	• Introduces use of term "innovation" to the standard.
	• Lack of management representative for assignments.
	• Old duties can be spread among top management.

ISO 14001:2015—Section 5.3
Organizational roles, responsibilities and authorities

Ensure responsibilities and authorities for relevant roles are assigned, communicated, and understood.

> Assign responsibility
> and authority to:

Ensure conformance to ISO 14001

Ensure processes are delivering intended outputs

Report on performance, opportunities for improvement, and need for change

Ensure promotion of customer focus

Ensure integrity of system

Changes from ISO 14001:2004:

- This clause replaces old clause 4.4.1 on responsibility and authority.
- Adds that responsibilities must be assigned and understood.
- Identifies some specific responsibilities to be assigned.
- Introduces use of term "innovation" to the standard.
- Lack of management representative for assignments.
- Old duties can be spread among top management.
- Innovation is defined as the process resulting in a new or substantially changed object, which can be a management system, a process, a product, a service, or technology.

UPDATES TO ISO 14001:2004 IN ISO 14001:2015

(Source: L. Whittington)

5. Leadership

5.1 Leadership and Commitment

The ISO 14001:2015 standard adds another way that top management must demonstrate its leadership and commitment—by taking accountability for the effectiveness of the environmental management system.

5.2 Environmental Policy

The policy commitment to meet requirements has been clarified as conforming to compliance obligations. The commitment for continual improvement has been clarified as improving the environmental management system to enhance environmental performance. A third policy commitment has been added: to protect the environment, including prevention of pollution.

A Note at this clause states other policy commitments might include sustainable resource use, climate change mitigation and adaptation, and protection of biodiversity and ecosystems. The standard adds that the policy must be communicated not just to employees, but also to persons doing work under the organization's control.

5.3 Organizational Roles, Responsibilities and Authorities

The ISO 14001:2015 standard clarifies that responsibilities and authorities are assigned and communicated to facilitate effective environmental management. It also adds that reporting on the performance of the system to top management includes reporting on environmental performance.

CLAUSE 6: PLANNING

6.1 Actions to address risks and opportunities
6.2 Environmental objectives and planning to achieve them

Overview: With the organization having highlighted the issues and requirements in clause 4, now is the time to address the risks and opportunities the organization faces by means of "planning." How will the organization prevent or reduce undesired effects? How will it ensure it can achieve its intended outcomes and improvement continually? It will do it here, in planning.

The Standard: 6.0 Planning

6.1 Actions to address risks and opportunities

6.1.1 General

Organizations are required to consider their context when planning for their environmental management systems. This means thinking about the internal and external issues they face and the relevant requirements of their relevant interested parties, and how these issues may impact their environmental management system design.

The organization must then move on to determine the risks and opportunities that need to be addressed within its given context. This is in order to provide assurance that the environmental management system can achieve its intended outcomes, to prevent or reduce undesired effects, and to achieve continual improvement.

Documented Information:

Required:

6.1.1—General

Cross-Reference 2004:

New requirement

Internal Audit Questions:	*Management:*
Internal auditors may ask: • Has the organization established, implemented, and maintained the processes needed to meet the requirements in 6.1.1 to 6.1.4? • When planning the EMS, has the organization considered the: a) Issues referred to in 4.1? b) Requirements referred to in 4.2? c) Scope of its EMS?	Changes: • Give assurance that the environmental management system can achieve its intended results. • Prevent, or reduce, undesired effects. • Achieve continual improvement.

ISO 14001:2015—Section 6.1
Actions to address risks and opportunities

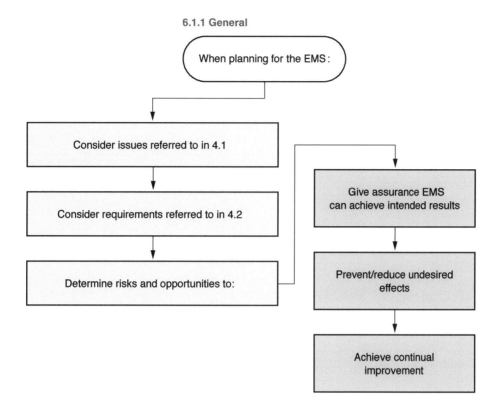

6.1.1 General

When planning for the EMS:

Consider issues referred to in 4.1

Consider requirements referred to in 4.2

Determine risks and opportunities to:

Give assurance EMS can achieve intended results

Prevent/reduce undesired effects

Achieve continual improvement

Additions to ISO 14001:2004:

Consistent and predictable results are achieved more effectively and efficiently when activities are understood and managed as interrelated processes that function as a coherent system. According to the draft ISO 14001:2015 standard, management of these processes and the system as a whole can be achieved using a plan–do–check–act (PDCA) methodology, with an overall focus on "risk-based thinking" aimed at preventing undesirable outcomes.

Risk is often expressed in terms of a combination of the consequences of an event, including changes in circumstances and the associated likelihood of occurrence. The term "risk" is sometimes used when there is only the possibility of negative consequences.

The Standard: 6.0 Planning

6.1 Actions to address risks and opportunities

6.1.2 Environmental aspects

Once the organization has identified the risks and opportunities it faces, it must then determine how it wishes to address these.

There is a statement regarding proportionality to the effect that actions taken to address risks and opportunities should be in line with the potential impact of the risk or opportunity on the conformity of products and/or services, as well as on customer satisfaction.

Documented Information:

Required:

6.1.2—Environmental aspects and impacts

Cross-Reference 2004:

4.3.1 Environmental aspects

Internal Audit Questions:	*Management:*
Internal auditors may ask:	Changes:
• Within the defined scope of the EMS, has the organization determined:	• Integrate and implement the actions into its environmental management system processes (see 4.4).
a) The environmental aspects of its activities, products, and services that it can control and those that it can influence?	• Evaluate the effectiveness of these actions.
b) Their associated environmental impacts, considering a life cycle perspective?	

ISO 14001:2015—Section 6.1
Actions to address risks and opportunities

6.1.2 Environmental aspects

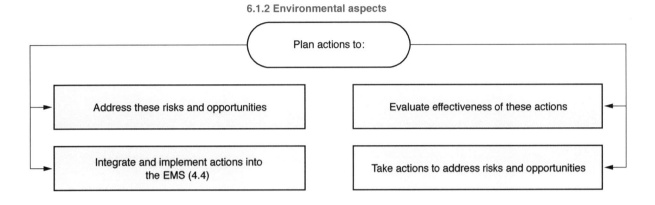

Plan actions to:

| Address these risks and opportunities | Evaluate effectiveness of these actions |
| Integrate and implement actions into the EMS (4.4) | Take actions to address risks and opportunities |

Options to address risks and opportunities

- Avoid risk
- Eliminate risk source
- Share risk
- Take risk to pursue opportunity
- Change likelihood or consequences
- Retain risk by informed decision

Annex A risk-based approach:

Annex A provides a clarification of the draft standard's new structure, terminology, and concepts. Annex A.4 states that the draft standard requires the organization to understand its context and determine the risks and opportunities that need to be addressed (see clause 6.1).

One of the key purposes of an environmental management system is to act as a preventive tool. Consequently, the draft standard does not have a separate clause or sub-clause titled "Preventive Action." The concept of preventive action is expressed through a risk-based approach to formulating environmental management system requirements.

The risk-based approach of the revised standard has facilitated some reduction in prescriptive requirements and their replacement by performance-based requirements.

Additions to ISO 14001:2004:

All processes of a system do not represent the same level of risk in terms of the organization's ability to meet its objectives. The consequences of process, product, service, or system nonconformities are not the same for all organizations. For some organizations, the consequences of delivering nonconforming products and services can result in minor inconvenience to the customer; for others, the consequences can be far-reaching and even fatal.

The Standard: 6.0 Planning

6.1 Actions to address risks and opportunities

6.1.3 Compliance obligations

Once the organization has identified the risks and opportunities it faces, it must then determine how it wishes to address these.

There is a statement regarding proportionality to the effect that actions taken to address risks and opportunities should be in line with the potential impact of the risk or opportunity on the conformity of products and/or services, as well as on customer satisfaction.

Documented Information:

Required:

6.1.3—Compliance obligations

Cross-Reference 2004:

4.3.2 Legal and other requirements

Internal Audit Questions:	Management:

Internal auditors may ask:
 	
• Has the organization:
 	
  a) Determined its compliance obligations related to its environmental aspects?
 	
  b) Determined how these compliance obligations apply to the organization?
 	
  c) Taken these compliance obligations into account when establishing, implementing, maintaining, and continually improving its EMS?
 	
• Does the organization maintain documented information of its compliance obligations?
	Changes:
	
	• Integrate and implement the actions into its environmental management system processes (see 4.4).
	
	• Evaluate the effectiveness of these actions.

ISO 14001:2015—Section 6.1
Actions to address risks and opportunities

6.1.3 Compliance obligations

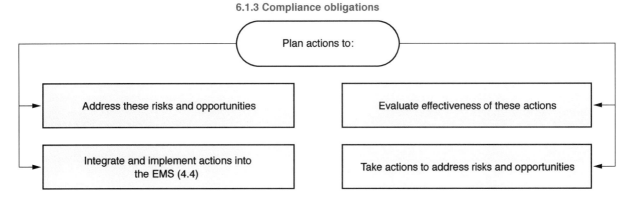

Options to address risks and opportunities

Annex A risk-based approach:

Annex A provides a clarification of the draft standard's new structure, terminology, and concepts. Annex A.4 states that the draft standard requires the organization to understand its context and determine the risks and opportunities that need to be addressed (see clause 6.1).

One of the key purposes of an environmental management system is to act as a preventive tool. Consequently, the draft standard does not have a separate clause or sub-clause titled "Preventive Action." The concept of preventive action is expressed through a risk-based approach to formulating environmental management system requirements.

The risk-based approach of the revised standard has facilitated some reduction in prescriptive requirements and their replacement by performance-based requirements.

Additions to ISO 14001:2004:

All processes of a system do not represent the same level of risk in terms of the organization's ability to meet its objectives. The consequences of process, product, service, or system nonconformities are not the same for all organizations. For some organizations, the consequences of delivering nonconforming products and services can result in minor inconvenience to the customer; for others, the consequences can be far-reaching and even fatal.

The Standard: 6.0 Planning

6.1 Actions to address risks and opportunities

6.1.4 Planning action

Once the organization has identified the risks and opportunities it faces, it must then determine how it wishes to address these.

There is a statement regarding proportionality to the effect that actions taken to address risks and opportunities should be in line with the potential impact of the risk or opportunity on the conformity of products and/or services, as well as on customer satisfaction.

Documented Information:

Required:

None

Cross-Reference 2004:

New requirement

Internal Audit Questions:	Management:

Internal auditors may ask:
 	
• Does the organization plan to take actions to address its:
 	
  a) Significant environmental aspects?
 	
  b) Compliance obligations?
 	
  c) Risks and opportunities identified in 6.1.1?
 	
• When planning these actions, does the organization consider its technological options and its financial, operational, and business requirements?
	Changes:
	
	• Integrate and implement the actions into its environmental management system processes (see 4.4).
	
	• Evaluate the effectiveness of these actions.

ISO 14001:2015—Section 6.1
Actions to address risks and opportunities

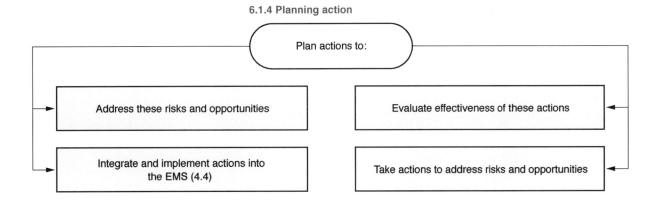

6.1.4 Planning action

Plan actions to:

Address these risks and opportunities	Evaluate effectiveness of these actions
Integrate and implement actions into the EMS (4.4)	Take actions to address risks and opportunities

Options to address risks and opportunities

Avoid risk

Eliminate risk source

Share risk

Take risk to pursue opportunity

Change likelihood or consequences

Retain risk by informed decision

Annex A risk-based approach:

Annex A provides a clarification of the draft standard's new structure, terminology, and concepts. Annex A.4 states that the draft standard requires the organization to understand its context and determine the risks and opportunities that need to be addressed (see clause 6.1).

One of the key purposes of an environmental management system is to act as a preventive tool. Consequently, the draft standard does not have a separate clause or sub-clause titled "Preventive Action." The concept of preventive action is expressed through a risk-based approach to formulating environmental management system requirements.

The risk-based approach of the revised standard has facilitated some reduction in prescriptive requirements and their replacement by performance-based requirements.

Additions to ISO 14001:2004:

All processes of a system do not represent the same level of risk in terms of the organization's ability to meet its objectives. The consequences of process, product, service, or system nonconformities are not the same for all organizations. For some organizations, the consequences of delivering nonconforming products and services can result in minor inconvenience to the customer; for others, the consequences can be far-reaching and even fatal.

The Standard: 6.0 Planning

6.2 Environmental objectives and planning to achieve them

6.2.1 Environmental objectives

The environmental objectives must be consistent with the organization's environmental policy and be relevant to the conformity of products and services, and the enhancement of customer satisfaction.

Environmental objectives must be measurable, take into account applicable customer and statutory and regulatory requirements, and be monitored in order to determine whether they are being met.

The objectives must also be communicated across the organization and updated as and when the need arises.

Documented Information:

Required:

6.2.1—Environmental objectives

Cross-Reference 2004:

4.3.3 Objectives, targets and programs

Internal Audit Questions:	Management:
Internal auditors may ask:	Changes:
• Have environmental objectives been established at relevant functions and levels?	• This clause replaces old clause 4.3.3 on environmental objectives.
• Do the objectives take into account the organization's significant environmental aspects and associated compliance obligations?	• Expands to set environmental objectives for relevant processes.
• Do the objectives consider the organization's risks and opportunities?	• Relevant to products, services, and customer satisfaction.
• Are the environmental objectives:	• Must consider objectives for applicable requirements.
a) Consistent with the environmental policy?	• Adds how to plan for achievement of environmental objectives.
b) Measurable (if practical)?	

ISO 14001:2015—Section 6.2.1
Environmental objectives and planning to achieve them

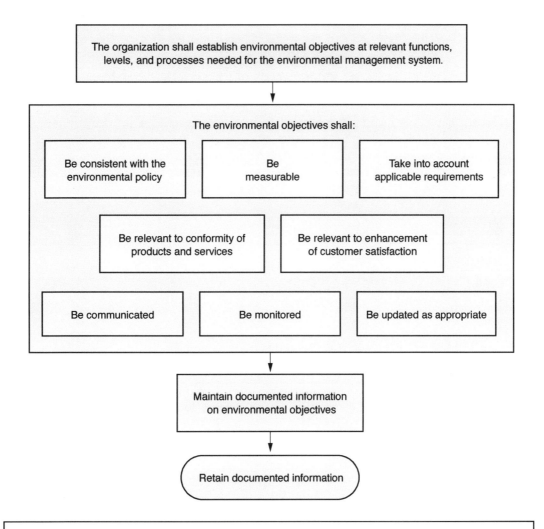

Changes from ISO 14001:2004:

• This clause (6.2.1) replaces old clause 4.3.3 (environmental objectives).

• Environmental objectives must be established at relevant functions, levels, and processes within the organization.

• Environmental objectives must be relevant to the products and/or services provided by the organization and be relevant to the enhancement of customer satisfaction.

• Environmental objectives must also take into account applicable requirements (internal and external).

The Standard: 6.0 Planning

6.2 Environmental objectives and planning to achieve them

6.2.2 Planning actions to achieve environmental objectives

The environmental objectives must be consistent with the organization's environmental policy and be relevant to the conformity of products and services, and the enhancement of customer satisfaction.

Environmental objectives must be measurable, take into account applicable customer and statutory and regulatory requirements, and be monitored in order to determine whether they are being met.

The objective must also be communicated across the organization and be updated as and when the need arises.

Documented Information:

Required:

None

Cross-Reference 2004:

4.3.3 Objectives, targets and programs

Internal Audit Questions:	Management:
Internal auditors may ask:	Changes:
• When planning how to achieve its environmental objectives, does the organization determine:	• New requirement.
a) What will be done?	• Expands to set environmental objectives for relevant processes.
b) What resources will be required?	• Relevant to products, services, and customer satisfaction.
c) Who will be responsible?	• Must consider objectives for applicable requirements.
d) When it will be completed?	• Adds how to plan for achievement of environmental objectives.
e) How the results will be evaluated, including indicators for monitoring progress toward achievement of its measurable environmental objectives (see 9.1.1)?	

ISO 14001:2015—Section 6.2.2
Environmental objectives and planning to achieve them

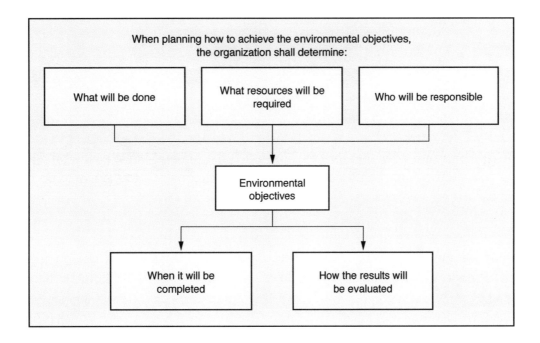

Changes from ISO 14001:2004:

• The requirement for planning how to achieve the environmental objectives is a new requirement.

UPDATES TO ISO 14001:2004 IN ISO 14001:2015

(Source: L. Whittington)

6. Planning

6.1 Actions to Address Risks and Opportunities

ISO 14001:2015 split this clause into four sub-clauses.

6.1.1 General

The ISO 14001:2015 standard adds that the organization is to plan and implement a process to meet the requirements in clause 6.1. Documented information is to be maintained to the extent necessary to have confidence that the process has been carried out as planned.

6.1.2 Environmental Aspects

The standard adds that the organization must identify the environmental aspects and impacts of the activities, products, and services that it can control and those it can influence, considering a life cycle perspective. Changes and identified abnormal and potential emergency situations are to be taken into account.

Those aspects that have or can have a significant impact on the environment must be determined. These significant environmental aspects must be communicated throughout the organization.

Documented information must be kept on environmental aspects and associated environmental impacts, the significant environmental aspects, and the criteria used to determine the significant environmental aspects.

6.1.3 Compliance Obligations

ISO 14001:2015 adds that the organization must identify and have access to the compliance obligations related to its environmental aspects, and determine how these compliance obligations apply to the organization. Note: The wording in sub-clauses 6.1.1, 6.1.2, and 6.1.3 is very similar to the wording in ISO 14001:2004, with almost no Annex SL text, except for some general references in 6.1.1.

6.1.4 Planning Action

The ISO 14001:2015 standard adds that the organization must plan for actions to address risk associated with threats and opportunities, significant environmental aspects (6.1.2), and compliance obligations (6.1.3).

The interpretive guidance in Annex A states that it is up to the organization to decide if it wishes to implement different risk evaluation processes at different organizational levels, or to combine all the risk evaluation requirements into a single process.

6.2 Environmental Objectives and Planning to Achieve Them

6.2.1 Environmental Objectives

The additions to the core Annex SL text for this sub-clause are about taking into account the organization's significant environmental aspects and its compliance obligations when establishing the environmental objectives. The organization is also to consider the risk associated with threats and opportunities when setting its environmental objectives.

When developing these objectives, the organization must consider its technological options and financial, operational, and business requirements.

6.2.2 Planning Actions to Achieve Environmental Objectives

The ISO 14001:2015 standard adds that when deciding how results will be evaluated, the organization must include indicators for monitoring progress toward achievement of measurable environmental objectives. The standard also states that the organization is to consider how the action to achieve environmental objectives can be integrated into its business processes.

CLAUSE 7: SUPPORT

7.1 Resources
7.2 Competence
7.3 Awareness
7.4 Communication
7.5 Documented information

Overview: The organization needs to consider the need for both internal and external communications relevant to the management system—what, when, and with whom it will communicate—as well as how it will communicate.

The Standard: 7.0 Support

7.1 Resources

The standard requires an organization initially to determine and then subsequently provide the resources necessary to establish, implement, maintain, and continually improve its environmental management system.

In doing so, the organization is required to consider both the capabilities and constraints on its existing internal resources as well as what needs to be sourced from external providers.

Documented Information:

Required:

None

Cross-Reference 2004:

4.4.1 Resources, roles, responsibility and authority

Internal Audit Questions:	Management:
Internal auditors may ask: • Has the organization determined and provided the resources needed for the establishment, implementation, maintenance, and continual improvement of the EMS?	Changes: • This clause updates old clause 6.1 on Resources. • It removes any mention of resources for customer satisfaction. • Customer satisfaction is mentioned at multiple clauses, including 9.1.2. • Adds consideration of internal resources and external providers.

ISO 14001:2015—Section 7.1
Resources

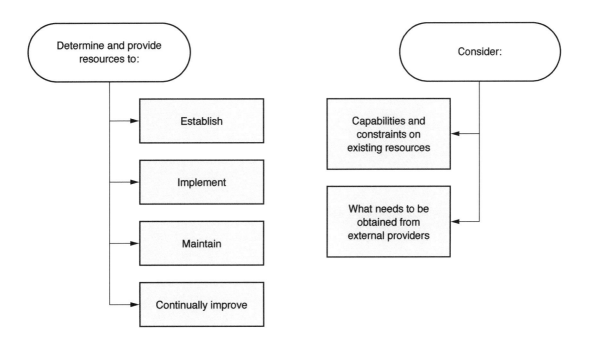

Determine and provide resources to:
- Establish
- Implement
- Maintain
- Continually improve

Consider:
- Capabilities and constraints on existing resources
- What needs to be obtained from external providers

Comment

There are other references to resources throughout the standard, for example:

5.1.d—Top management ensuring resources are available

6.2.2.b—Resources needed to achieve environmental objectives

9.3—Management review of resource needs for changes

9.3.e—Management review of adequacy of resources

Changes from ISO 14001:2004:

- This clause updates old clause 6.1 on Resources.

- It removes any mention of resources for customer satisfaction.

- Customer satisfaction is mentioned in multiple clauses, including 9.1.2.

- Adds consideration of internal resources and external providers.

The Standard: 7.0 Support

7.2 Competence

The organization must determine the competency requirements for those people performing work under its control.

Once these competency requirements have been determined, the organization must then ensure that those people possess the necessary competencies, either on the basis of their education, training, or experience.

The organization is required to take action to acquire the necessary competence. Actions taken need to be evaluated for effectiveness.

Documented Information:

Required:

7.2—Training evidence

Cross-Reference 2004:

4.4.2 Competence, training and awareness

Internal Audit Questions:	Management:

Internal auditors may ask:
 	
• Has the organization:
 	
  a) Determined the necessary competence of persons doing work under its control that affects its environmental performance and its ability to fulfill compliance obligations?
 	
  b) Ensured that these persons are competent on the basis of appropriate education, training, or experience?
 	
  c) Determine training needs associated with its environmental aspects and its EMS?
 	
  d) Where applicable, taken actions to acquire the necessary competence and evaluate the effectiveness of the actions taken?
	Changes:
	
	• This clause replaces most of old clause 6.2 on Human Resources.
	
	• Old clause 6.2.2.d is now in new clause 7.3 on Awareness.
	
	• Use of "under its control" includes contract, agency, and outsourcing.
	
	• See new clause 8.1 on competence of external providers.
	
	• The clause adds a Note with examples of applicable actions.

ISO 14001:2015—Section 7.2
Competence

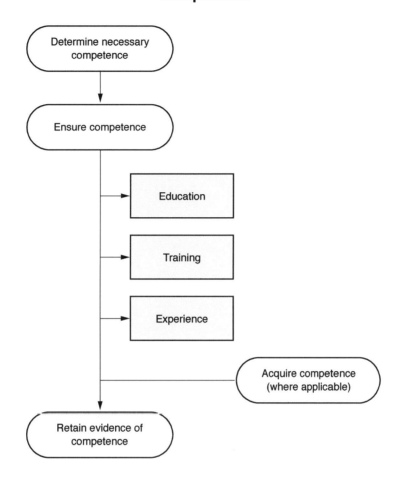

Note

Applicable actions can include, for example, training, mentoring, or reassignment of currently employed persons, or hiring or contracting of competent persons.

Changes from ISO 14001:2004:

- This clause replaces most of old clause 6.2 on Human Resources.

- Old clause 6.2.2.d is now in new clause 7.3 on Awareness.

- Use of "under its control" includes contract, agency, and outsourcing.

- See new clause 8.1 on competence of external providers.

- The clause adds a Note with examples of applicable actions.

- "Competence" is defined in the terms section as the ability to apply knowledge and skills to achieve intended results. Demonstrated competence is sometimes referred to as "qualification."

The Standard: 7.0 Support

7.3 Awareness

The requirements contained in the new clause 7.3 now apply to all "persons doing work under the organization's control." This is more expansive than under ISO 14001:2004 where the organization needed to ensure that "its personnel" were aware.

There are explicit requirements for people doing work under the organization's control to be aware of the organization's environmental policy, any environmental objectives that are relevant to them, how they are contributing to the effectiveness of the EMS, and what the implications are of them not conforming to EMS requirements.

Documented Information:

Required:

None

Cross-Reference 2004:

4.4.2 Competence, training and awareness

Internal Audit Questions:	Management:
Internal auditors may ask:	Changes:
• Has the organization ensured that persons doing work under the organization's control are aware of:	• Elevates the old sub-clause 6.2.2.d to a separate clause.
a) The environmental policy?	• Expands personnel to include persons under the organization's control.
b) The significant environmental aspects and related actual or potential environmental impacts associated with their work?	• Awareness now covers the environmental policy and objectives.
c) Their contribution to the effectiveness of the EMS, including the benefits of enhanced environmental performance?	• Adds awareness of the implications of not meeting requirements.
d) The implications of not conforming with the EMS requirements, including not fulfilling the organization's compliance obligations?	

ISO 14001:2015—Section 7.3
Awareness

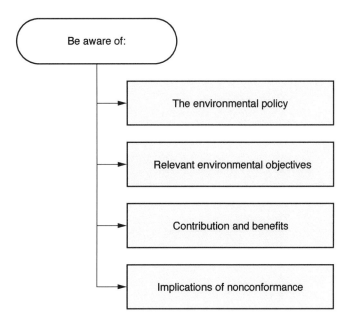

Changes from ISO 14001:2004:

• Elevates the old sub-clause 6.2.2.d to a separate clause.

• Expands personnel to include persons under the organization's control.

• Awareness now covers the environmental policy and objectives.

• Adds awareness of the implications of not meeting requirements.

The Standard: 7.0 Support

7.4 Communication

7.4.1 General

7.4.2 Internal communication

7.4.3 External communication

Communication encompasses all internal and external communication relating to an organization's EMS.

Each organization must determine those EMS-related matters on which it wishes to communicate.

Once this has been done, consideration must then be given to the timing of such communications, their target audience, and their method of delivery.

Documented Information:

Required:

7.4.1—Evidence of communication

Cross-Reference 2004:

4.4.3 Communication

Internal Audit Questions:	Management:
Internal auditors may ask:	Changes:
• Has the organization established, implemented, and maintained the processes needed for internal and external communications relevant to the EMS, including: a) On what it will communicate? b) When to communicate? c) With whom to communicate? d) How to communicate?	• This clause replaces the old clause 4.4.3 on internal communication. • Requirement is more explicit: what, when, whom, and how. • Requirement has expanded to include "external" communication. • "Customer" communication was moved from old clause 4.4.3 to new 7.4.3.

ISO 14001:2015—Section 7.4
Communication

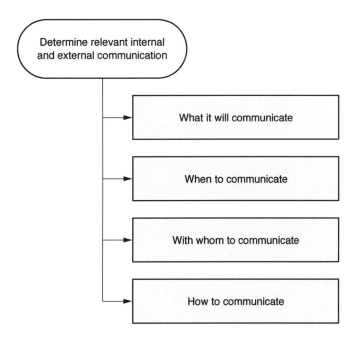

Changes from ISO 14001:2004:

• This clause replaces old clause 4.4.3 on internal communication.

• The requirement is more explicit: what, when, whom, and how.

• The requirement has expanded to include "external" communication.

• "Customer" communication was moved from old clause 4.4.3 to new clause 7.4.3.

The Standard: 7.0 Support

7.5 Documented information

7.5.1 General

This clause requires that an organization's environmental management system include both documented information identified as required in the standard and documented information identified by the organization as necessary for the effective operation of its environmental management system.

Documented Information:

Required:

7.5.1a,b—Required by standard

Cross-Reference 2004:

4.4.4 Documentation

Internal Audit Questions:	Management:

Internal auditors may ask:
 	
• Does the organization's EMS include:
 	
  a) Documented information required by ISO 14001:2015?
 	
  b) Documented information determined by the organization as being necessary for the effectiveness of the EMS?
	Changes:
	
	• Replaces old clauses 4.2.1.c and 4.2.1.d on documentation requirements.
	
	• Changes from "procedures" and "records" to "documented information."
	
	• The Note on "extent" is from Note 2 in old clause 4.2.1.

ISO 14001:2015—Section 7.5
Documented information

7.5.1 General

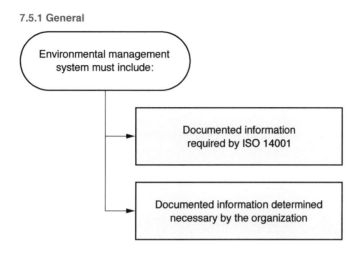

Note

The extent of documented information can differ from one organization to another due to the:

a) Size of the organization and its type of activities, processes, products, and services

b) Complexity of processes and their interactions

c) Competence of persons

Changes from ISO 14001:2004:

• Replaces old clauses 4.2.1.c and 4.2.1.d on documentation requirements.

• Changes from "procedures" and "records" to "documented information."

• The Note on "extent" is from Note 2 in old clause 4.2.1.

The Standard: 7.0 Support

7.5 Documented information

7.5.2 Creating and updating

When documented information is created or updated, the organization must ensure that it is appropriately identified and described (e.g., title, date, author, reference number).

It must be in an appropriate format (e.g., language, software version, graphics) and on appropriate media (e.g., paper, electronic).

Documented information must be reviewed and approved for suitability and adequacy.

Documented Information:

Required:

7.5.2—Document identification

Cross-Reference 2004:

4.4.5 Control of documents

4.5.4 Control of records

Internal Audit Questions:	*Management:*

Internal auditors may ask:
 	
• When creating and updating documented information, does the organization ensure appropriate:
 	
  a) Identification and description (e.g., a title, date, author, or reference number)?
 	
  b) Format (e.g., language, software version, graphics) and media (e.g., paper, electronic)?
 	
  c) Review and approval for suitability and adequacy?
	Changes:
	
	• Gathered requirements from old clause 4.2.3.a, b, c, and e.
	
	• New clause adds examples: description, format, and media.

ISO 14001:2015—Section 7.5
Documented information

7.5.2 Creating and updating documentation

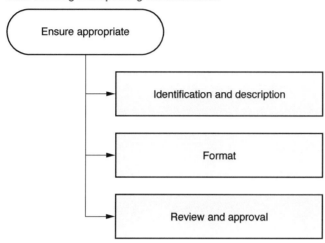

Changes from ISO 14001:2004:

• Gathered requirements from old clause 4.2.3 (a, b, c, and e).

• New clause adds examples: description, format, and media.

The Standard: 7.0 Support

7.5 Documented information

7.5.3 Control of documented information

The organization is required to control documented information in order to ensure that it is available where needed and that it is suitable for use. It must also be adequately protected against improper use, loss of integrity, and loss of confidentiality.

The organization must determine how it will distribute, access, retrieve, and use documented information.

It must decide how it will store and preserve documented information, and how it will control any changes to the documented information. It must also decide its retention and disposal arrangements.

The organization is also required to identify any documented information of external origin to the organization that it considers necessary for the planning and operation of the organization's environmental management system. Such documentation must be identified and controlled.

Documented Information:

Required:

7.5.3—Document control

7.5.3—Control process

7.5.3—External documents (see also the Note)

Cross-Reference 2004:

4.4.5 Control of documents

4.5.4 Control of records

Internal Audit Questions:	Management:

Internal auditors may ask:
 	
• Is the documented information required by the EMS and by ISO 14001:2015 controlled to ensure:
 	
  a) It is available and suitable for use, where and when it is needed?
 	
  b) It is adequately protected (e.g., from loss of confidentiality, improper use, or loss of integrity)?
	Changes:
	
	• Gathered from old clause 4.2.3 (c, d, e, f) on control of documents.
	
	• Includes requirements from old clause 4.2.4 on control of records.
	
	• No mention of obsolete documents; covered by version control.
	
	• Adds Note on types of access to documented information.
	
	• Also see Annex A.7.5 on Documented information.

ISO 14001:2015—Section 7.5
Documented information

7.5.3 Control of documented information

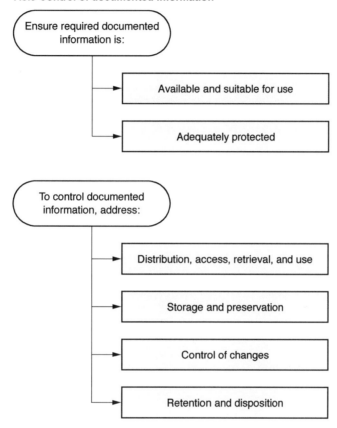

Note

- Documented information of external origin determined by the organization to be necessary for the planning and operation of the system must be identified as appropriate, and controlled.

- Access can imply a decision regarding the permission to view the documented information only, or the permission and authority to view and change the documented information.

Changes from ISO 14001:2004:

- Gathered from old clause 4.2.3 (c, d, e, and f) on control of documents.

- Includes requirements from old clause 4.2.4 on control of records.

- No mention of obsolete documents; covered by version control.

- Adds Note on types of access to documented information.

- Also see Annex A.7.5 on Documented information.

UPDATES TO ISO 14001:2004 IN ISO 14001:2015

(Source: L. Whittington)

7. Support

7.1 Resources

See additions to the Annex SL text for resources.

7.2 Competence

See additions to the Annex SL text for competence.

7.3 Awareness

The only ISO 14001:2015 addition to this clause is that persons doing work under the organization's control must be aware of the significant environmental aspects and related actual or potential impacts associated with their work. These persons must also be aware of the implications of not conforming to the environmental management system requirements, including compliance obligations.

7.4 Communication

The ISO 14001:2015 standard has expanded this Communication clause into three sub-clauses.

7.4.1 General

The standard adds that when planning its communication process, the organization must take into account its compliance obligations, and ensure that reliable environmental information is communicated consistent with the information generated by its environmental management system.

   The organization must also respond to relevant communications on its environmental management system and retain documented information as evidence of its communications.

7.4.2 Internal Communication

ISO 14001:2015 adds that the organization must communicate among its various levels and functions any changes to the environmental management system. The standard also states that the organization must ensure its communication process enables any person doing work under its control to contribute to continual improvement.

7.4.3 External Communication

ISO 14001:2015 adds that the organization must externally communicate information relevant to the environmental management system as determined by its communication process and as required by its compliance obligations.

7.5 Documented Information

7.5.1 General

7.5.2 Creating and Updating

7.5.3 Control of Documented Information

For the most part organizations with a solid document control process in place will satisfy the new standard.

Remember, the shift in thinking is away from "document control" and now toward "documented information" (i.e., video instructions, sound commands, color codes, etc.).

There are no additions to the Annex SL text for these three sub-clauses on documented information.

CLAUSE 8: OPERATION

8.1 Operational planning and control
8.2 Emergency preparedness and response

Overview: Whatever the organization is in business to achieve, clause 8 supports it. At its core, the organization needs to ". . . plan, implement and control the processes needed." This addresses both in-house and any outsourced processes. The overall process management includes having process criteria, controlling the processes within the criteria, planning change, and addressing unintended change as necessary.

The Standard: 8.0 Operation

8.1 Operational planning and control

This clause requires organizations to plan, implement, and control those processes that it has previously identified (see clause 4.4) in order for it to meet the EMS requirements and to implement the actions identified in 6.1 and 6.2. To do so, organizations have to establish operating criteria for those processes and implement control of the processes in accordance with these operating criteria.

The organization must control planned changes to its EMS and review the consequences of any unintended changes. Where necessary, the organization should take action to address or mitigate any adverse effects. In relation to outsourced processes, the organization has to ensure that they are controlled or influenced. The definition of outsource, as a verb, is "to make an arrangement where an external provider performs part of an organization's function or process."

Organizations need to consider life cycles in the planning process. What is a life cycle? It is a set of consecutive and interlinked stages of a product (or service) system, from raw material acquisition or its generation from natural resources to final disposal.

Documented Information:

Required:

8.1—Process confidence (evidence of . . .)

Cross-Reference 2004:

4.4.6 Operational control

Internal Audit Questions:	*Management:*
Internal auditors may ask:	Changes:
• Has the organization established, implemented, controlled, and maintained the processes needed to meet EMS requirements?	• Tie in risk. Plan, implement, and control the processes, as outlined in 4.4, needed to meet requirements for the provision of products and services and to implement the actions determined in 6.1.
• Has the organization implemented the actions determined in 6.1 and 6.2 by:	• Controls can include engineering controls and procedures. Controls can be implemented following a hierarchy (e.g., elimination, substitution, administrative) and can be used individually or in combination.
a) Establishing operating criteria for the processes?	
b) Implementing control of the processes in accordance with the operating criteria?	

ISO 14001:2015—Section 8.1
Operational planning and control

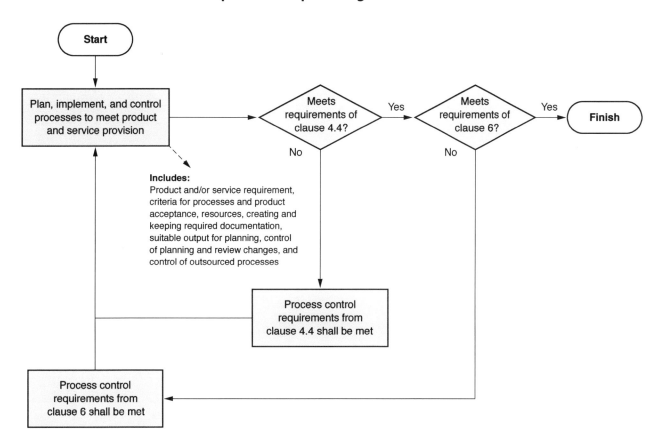

Note

"Keeping" implies both the maintaining and the retaining of documented information.

Changes from ISO 14001:2004:

• Clause 8.1 replaces clause 7.1 of the 9000:2004 standard, Product Realization. The clause provides for additional control and planning of products and services by requiring determination of process criteria and the resources to achieve the intended results from operational processes. Clause 8.1 requires that there are controlled methods for adopting changes to the developed processes and product/service requirements.

• The clause also requires that the required documentation be determined and kept to provide adequate confidence that the planned activities and results from the controlled processes will be achieved, as well as how any existing documentation will be modified.

The Standard: 8.0 Operation

8.2 Emergency preparedness and response

The standard requires the organization to establish, implement, and maintain processes to prepare for emergency situations and to respond if they occur. This is one of the few instances where specific processes are mandated.

The emergency situations to be covered are those identified in 6.1.1. These may originate within the organization and have the potential to affect the environment, or may be an environmental condition that has the potential to affect the organization. The organization has to ensure that these processes are ready to be triggered and that it has the capability to respond effectively to emergency situations.

In order to do so, the planned response actions need to be tested, reviewed, and revised if necessary, in particular after the occurrence of emergency situations and after tests. Interested parties need to be made aware of these arrangements and, when necessary, trained if they are required to participate in the emergency response or if they may be affected by the emergency situation.

Documented Information:

Required:

8.2—Process confidence (evidence of . . .)

Cross-Reference 2004:

4.4.7 Emergency preparedness and response

Internal Audit Questions:	*Management:*
Internal auditors may ask:	Changes:
• Has the organization established, implemented, and maintained the processes needed to prepare for and respond to potential emergency situations identified in 6.1.1?	• Ensure your organization maintains documented information to the extent necessary to have confidence that the processes are carried out as planned.
• Does the organization:	• Examples: Spill prevention, control, and countermeasure plan; site plan; evacuation plan; disaster response plan; active shooter plan.
a) Prepare to respond by planning actions to prevent or mitigate adverse environmental impacts from emergency situations?	
b) Respond to actual emergency situations?	
c) Take action to prevent or mitigate the consequences of emergency situations, appropriate to the magnitude of the emergency and the potential environmental impact?	
d) Periodically test the planned response actions, where practical?	

ISO 14001:2015—Section 8.2
Emergency preparedness and response

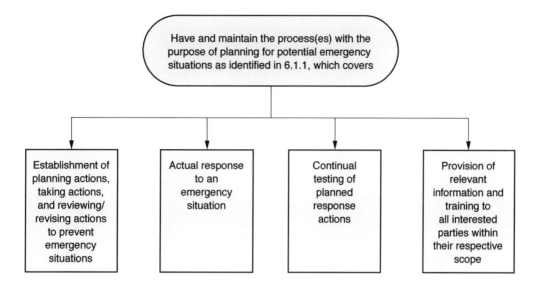

Have and maintain the process(es) with the purpose of planning for potential emergency situations as identified in 6.1.1, which covers

| Establishment of planning actions, taking actions, and reviewing/ revising actions to prevent emergency situations | Actual response to an emergency situation | Continual testing of planned response actions | Provision of relevant information and training to all interested parties within their respective scope |

Changes from ISO 14001:2004:

• The requirement is essentially the same as in the 2004 edition (4.4.7); however, it should be noted that the identification of potential emergency situations has been moved to clause 6.1.1 as part of the identification of risks.

• The emergency preparedness and response processes may include the training of emergency brigades, a list of key personnel and aid organizations (including contact details), evacuation routes and assembly points, and the possibility of assistance from neighboring organizations.

UPDATES TO ISO 14001:2004 IN ISO 14001:2015

(Source: L. Whittington)

8. Operation

8.1 Operational Planning and Control

The ISO 14001:2015 standard clarifies that operational controls are implemented to prevent deviation from the environmental policy and objectives as well as compliance obligations. It also states that the type and degree of control or influence of any outsourced processes must be defined within the environmental management system.

The concept of "life cycle perspective" is added that requires the organization to:

a) Determine environmental requirements for the procurement of its products and services.

b) Ensure environmental requirements are considered in the design, delivery, use, and end-of-life treatment of its products and services.

c) Communicate relevant environmental requirements to suppliers and contractors.

d) Provide information about potential environmental impacts during the delivery of products or services during use and end-of-life treatment of the product.

8.2 Emergency Preparedness and Response

This clause is not part of Annex SL and has been added by the ISO 14001:2015 standard. It is basically the same content as in clause 4.4.7 of the ISO 14001:2004 standard.

The requirement in the first paragraph of ISO 14001:2004 to identify emergency situations has been relocated to clause 8.2 of ISO 14001:2015.

CLAUSE 9: PERFORMANCE EVALUATION

9.1 Monitoring, measurement, analysis and evaluation
9.2 Internal audit
9.3 Management review

Overview: Internal audits carried out by the organization, or by an external party acting on the organization's behalf, provide information on whether the management system conforms to the requirements of the organization and the standard, and whether it is effectively implemented and maintained. Management review addresses the question: Is the management system suitable, adequate, and effective?

The Standard: 9.0 Performance Evaluation

9.1 Monitoring, measurement, analysis and evaluation

9.1.1 General

9.1.2 Evaluation of compliance

The organization has to initially determine what it needs to monitor and measure (e.g., its progress on environmental objectives, characteristics of operational activities, products and services related to significant environmental aspects or to compliance obligations). This includes the determination of the criteria against which the environmental performance will be evaluated, including appropriate indicators.

Once this has been done, the organization has to determine how it is going to carry out these monitoring and measurement activities in order to ensure that the results obtained are valid. The requirement for methods to ensure valid results also extends to the analysis and evaluation of the results obtained from the monitoring and measurement activities. These methods may include, as appropriate, statistical techniques to be applied to the analysis of those results.

Documented Information:

Required:

9.1.1—Monitoring evidence (key metric/indicators)

9.1.2—Compliance evaluation (evaluation of . . .)

Cross-Reference 2004:

4.5.1 Monitoring and measurement

4.5.2 Evaluation of compliance

Internal Audit Questions:	Management:

Internal auditors may ask:
 	
• Does the organization, monitor, measure, analyze, and evaluate its environmental performance?
 	
• Does the organization determine:
 	
  a) What needs to be monitored and measured?
 	
  b) The methods for monitoring, measurement, analysis, and evaluation, as applicable, to ensure valid results?
 	
  c) The criteria against which the organization will evaluate its environmental performance, and appropriate indicators?
 	
• Has the organization established, implemented, and maintained the processes needed to evaluate fulfillment of its compliance obligations?
	Changes:
	
	• Ensure that monitoring and measurement activities are implemented in accordance with determined requirements and retain documented information as evidence of the results. Evaluate the environmental performance and effectiveness of the environmental management system.

ISO 9001:2015—Section 9.1
Monitoring, measurement, analysis and evaluation

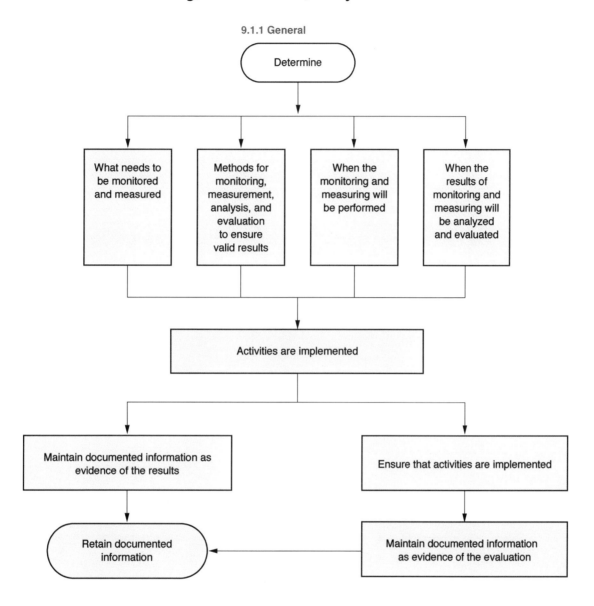

9.1.1 General

Determine

What needs to be monitored and measured

Methods for monitoring, measurement, analysis, and evaluation to ensure valid results

When the monitoring and measuring will be performed

When the results of monitoring and measuring will be analyzed and evaluated

Activities are implemented

Maintain documented information as evidence of the results

Ensure that activities are implemented

Retain documented information

Maintain documented information as evidence of the evaluation

Changes from ISO 14001:2004:

• This clause replaces old clause 4.5.1 and is now part of Performance Evaluation (Section 9).

• The organization determines the inputs to Performance Evaluation.

• The organization must identify when in the process monitoring and measuring activities are performed and the results evaluated.

• What is done with the results should relate to the performance and effectiveness of the management system.

• Auditors will need evidence of monitoring and review activities.

ISO 14001:2015—Section 9.1
Monitoring, measurement, analysis and evaluation

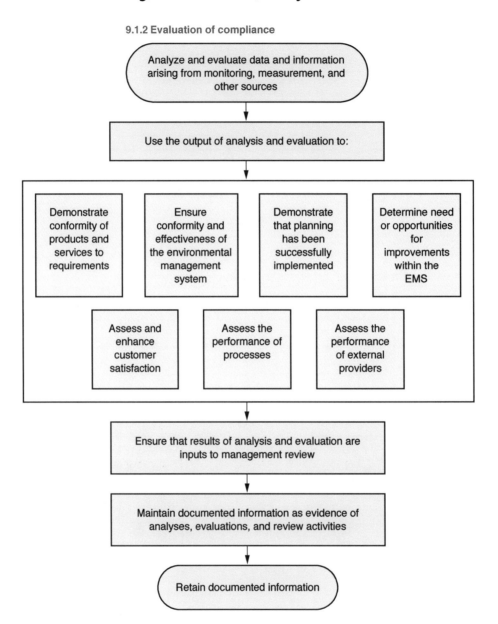

9.1.2 Evaluation of compliance

Analyze and evaluate data and information arising from monitoring, measurement, and other sources

↓

Use the output of analysis and evaluation to:

↓

Demonstrate conformity of products and services to requirements	Ensure conformity and effectiveness of the environmental management system	Demonstrate that planning has been successfully implemented	Determine need or opportunities for improvements within the EMS

Assess and enhance customer satisfaction	Assess the performance of processes	Assess the performance of external providers

↓

Ensure that results of analysis and evaluation are inputs to management review

↓

Maintain documented information as evidence of analyses, evaluations, and review activities

↓

Retain documented information

Changes from ISO 14001:2004:

• This clause replaces old clause 4.5.1 for monitoring and measurement.

• The demonstration that planning has been "successfully implemented" is a new requirement.

• The assessment of the performance of processes (including characteristics and trends) is a new requirement.

• The requirement to "assess and enhance customer satisfaction" goes beyond previous requirements.

• The requirement to "demonstrate conformity of products and services" goes beyond previous requirements.

• The requirement for "external providers" is not new, but suggests that more in-depth analyses be performed.

The Standard: 9.0 Performance Evaluation

9.2 Internal audit

9.2.1 General

9.2.2 Internal audit program

Ever present is the requirement for the organization to carry out internal audits at planned intervals in order to determine whether the environmental management system conforms to both the organization's own requirements and the requirements of the standard. Internal audits must also identify whether the environmental management system is being effectively implemented and maintained.

When designing an audit program, organizations need to consider their environmental objectives, the importance of the processes concerned, customer feedback, changes within the organization, risks and opportunities, and the results of previous audits.

Each audit needs to have a defined scope and its own audit criteria. Audits and auditors need to be impartial and objective. Finally, the findings from audits need to be fed back to the relevant management with any required corrections or corrective actions being taken in a timely manner.

Documented Information:

Required:

9.2.2—Audit program evidence (schedule, process matrix, records)

Cross-Reference 2004:

4.5.5 Internal audit

Internal Audit Questions:	Management:

Internal auditors may ask:
 	
• Do the audits provide information on whether the EMS:
 	
  a) Conforms to the organization's own requirements?
 	
  b) Conforms to the requirements of ISO 14001:2015?
 	
• Has the organization established, implemented, and maintained an internal audit program including the frequency, methods, responsibilities, planning requirements, and reporting of its internal audits?
 	
• When establishing the internal audit program, has the organization considered the environmental importance of the processes concerned?
	Changes:
	
	• Conduct internal audits at planned intervals to provide information on whether the environmental management system conforms to requirements.
	
	• Consider time-based tools like schedules as well as process tools like matrices.

ISO 14001:2015—Section 9.2
Internal audit

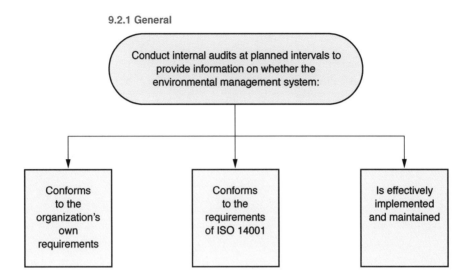

9.2.1 General

Conduct internal audits at planned intervals to provide information on whether the environmental management system:

| Conforms to the organization's own requirements | Conforms to the requirements of ISO 14001 | Is effectively implemented and maintained |

Changes from ISO 14001:2004:

• This clause (consisting of clauses 9.2.1 and 9.2.2) replaces and clarifies old clause 4.5.5 and is now part of Performance Evaluation (Section 9).

• The audit program must be defined to describe how it meets the requirements of the standard.

• The organization determines the frequency and scope of internal audits.

• Audits must be planned and scheduled to ensure compliance to the standard prescribed.

• The organization's requirements are established in the EMS.

• Auditors will need evidence of planning, execution, and review activities.

ISO 14001:2015—Section 9.2
Internal audit

9.2.2 Internal audit program

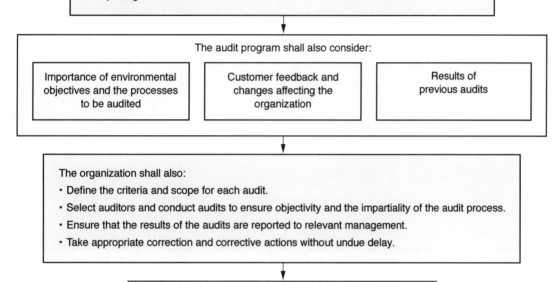

The organization shall plan, establish, and maintain an audit program(s) that includes:
- Frequency
- Methods
- Responsibilities
- Planning requirements
- Reporting

The audit program shall also consider:

| Importance of environmental objectives and the processes to be audited | Customer feedback and changes affecting the organization | Results of previous audits |

The organization shall also:
- Define the criteria and scope for each audit.
- Select auditors and conduct audits to ensure objectivity and the impartiality of the audit process.
- Ensure that the results of the audits are reported to relevant management.
- Take appropriate correction and corrective actions without undue delay.

Maintain documented information as evidence of the implementation of the audit program and the audit results

Retain documented information

Changes from ISO 14001:2004:

Environmental professionals should note that, while the detailed requirements for internal audits are essentially unchanged from ISO 14001:2004, there are two important revisions:

- In the 2004 version, the purpose of an internal audit is to "determine" whether the EMS is conforming to requirements and is effectively implemented and maintained (i.e., to actually make the judgment). In the 2015 version, the purpose of internal audits is to simply "provide information" as to whether this is the case. The determination is now done elsewhere (management review).

- The results of internal audits now need to be fed to "relevant management," not "management." Relevant management are those individuals in the best place to act on the audit findings. There is no longer a requirement for organizations to establish a documented internal audit procedure. However, organizations may still choose to operate one if they so wish.

The Standard: 9.0 Performance Evaluation

9.3 Management review

This clause requires reviews of the environmental management system to be undertaken by top management at planned intervals in order to ensure the environmental management system's continuing suitability, adequacy, and effectiveness. This is essentially unchanged.

Outputs must include decisions as to whether there is a need to change any aspect of the environmental management system including, but not limited to, the level of resources provided to support the operation of the EMS, as well as any decisions relating to continual improvement opportunities.

The organization must retain documented information to provide evidence as to the results of management reviews.

Documented Information:

Required:

9.3—Management review results

Cross-Reference 2004:

4.6 Management review

Internal Audit Questions:	Management:
Internal auditors may ask:	Changes:
• Does top management review the organization's EMS, at planned intervals, to ensure its continuing suitability, adequacy, effectiveness, and alignment with the strategic direction of the organization?	• Remember to review the environmental management system at planned intervals to ensure a suitable, adequate, and effective system aligned with the strategic direction of the organization.
• Does the management review consider:	• Be active with your EMS; do not just be informed or attend meetings, but take an action item and report back.
a) The status of actions from previous management reviews?	
b) Changes in external and internal issues that are relevant to the EMS?	
c) Changes in the needs and expectations of interested parties, including compliance obligations?	
d) Changes in significant environmental aspects?	
e) Changes in risks and opportunities?	

ISO 14001:2015—Section 9.3
Management review

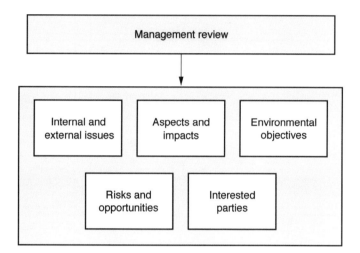

General

Top management shall review the organization's environmental management system, at planned intervals, to ensure its continuing suitability, adequacy, effectiveness, and alignment with the strategic direction of the organization.

Management review

Internal and external issues

Aspects and impacts

Environmental objectives

Risks and opportunities

Interested parties

Changes from ISO 14001:2004:

• This clause (9.3) replaces and clarifies old clause 4.6 and is now part of Performance Evaluation (Section 9).

• The organization determines the frequency and scope of management reviews.

• Each review does not have to be all-encompassing.

• Top management shall be engaged in the process.

• Management review planning (time and scope) and activities (review inputs) shall be aligned with the "strategic direction" of the organization.

• There is no requirement for a management review documented procedure.

• Auditors will need to see evidence of planning and execution of review activities.

ISO 14001:2015—Section 9.3
Management review

Management review inputs

Management review (inputs) shall consider:

| Status of actions from previous management reviews | Internal changes relevant to the environmental management system | External changes relevant to the environmental management system |

Information on the performance and effectiveness of the environmental management system, including trends in:

- Customer satisfaction and feedback from relevant interested parties
- The extent to which environmental objectives have been met
- Process performance and conformity of products and services
- Nonconformities and corrective actions
- Monitoring and measurement results
- Audit results
- The performance of external providers

| The adequacy of resources | The effectiveness of actions taken to address risks and opportunities | Opportunities for improvement |

→ Management review

Changes from ISO 14001:2004:

- All clause requirements (from old clause 4.6) have been retained.

- Some required inputs, such as to review "the status of actions from previous management reviews," have been reordered to reflect a more orderly flow (old business before new business).

- Some requirements have been reworded for clarification. As an example, "process performance and product conformity" from the old standard was revised to "process performance and conformity of products and services."

- Trending and/or performance data should be discussed.

- The requirement to review "the effectiveness of actions taken to address risks and opportunities" refers to the requirements of clause 6.1 and essentially replaces "preventive action" from the old standard.

ISO 14001:2015—Section 9.3
Management review

Management review outputs

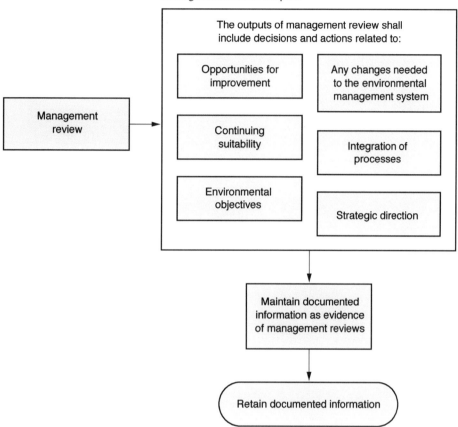

Changes from ISO 14001:2004:

• Changes in the context of the organization (it could be argued that "changing circumstances" in the previous edition was exactly this), the requirements of interested parties, the significant environmental impacts, the risks and opportunities, and the adequacy of resources all now need to be considered.

• This clause also sets out specific requirements regarding the outputs from management review. Is the EMS effective, suitable, and adequate? Is there any improvement opportunity to be implemented? Is there any need to change elements of the EMS? Is there a need for additional resources? Is there any need for action to address objectives that have not been met? Is there any way to improve the integration of the EMS with other business processes? Is there any implication for the strategic direction of the organization?

UPDATES TO ISO 14001:2004 IN ISO 14001:2015

(Source: L. Whittington)

9. Performance Evaluation

9.1 Monitoring, Measurement, Analysis and Evaluation

9.1.1 General

The ISO 14001:2015 standard adds to the Annex SL text that whatever needs to be monitored and measured must be related to operations (that can have a significant environmental impact), compliance obligations, operational controls, and progress toward meeting environmental objectives (using indicators). The ISO 14001:2004 standard did not explicitly require the use of indicators, although their use is widespread. Now it is a clear requirement.

ISO 14001:2015 also adds that the organization must determine the criteria for evaluating its environmental criteria through the use of appropriate indicators. The organization must communicate information relevant to its environmental performance both internally and externally, as determined by its communication process and as required by its compliance obligations.

9.1.2 Evaluation of Compliance

The requirement in clause 4.5.2 of ISO 14001:2004 to evaluate conformity with compliance obligations is still present. The ISO 14001:2015 standard requires the organization to determine the compliance evaluation frequency, evaluate compliance (and take action if needed), and maintain knowledge and understanding of its conformity status with compliance obligations.

9.2 Internal Audit

There are no major additions to the core Annex SL text for internal audit.

9.3 Management Review

ISO 14001:2015 adds that management reviews should consider changes in compliance obligations, significant environmental aspects, and risks associated with threats and opportunities. It also adds that the management reviews must consider communications from external interested parties, the adequacy of resources, and the extent to which objectives have been met.

The additional review outputs required by the standard are the conclusions on the continuing suitability, adequacy, and effectiveness of the environmental management system, as well as actions when objectives have not been met and any implications for the strategic direction of the organization.

CLAUSE 10: IMPROVEMENT

10.1 General
10.2 Nonconformity and corrective action
10.3 Continual improvement

Overview: The organization will benefit from an active and robust system where occasionally undesired things occur. It's time to address nonconformity and corrective action to make things better and achieve continual improvement.

The Standard: 10.0 Improvement

10.1 General

This is a new clause. It requires organizations to actively seek out and realize improvement opportunities that will better enable the organization to achieve the intended outcomes of the EMS.

Potential sources of improvement opportunities include the results of analysis and evaluation of environmental performance, evaluation of compliance, internal audits, and management reviews (i.e., clause 9).

Improvement may not always take place on a continual basis. Sometimes it occurs as a result of corrective action, sometimes through breakthrough/innovation, and sometimes as a result of reorganization.

Preventive action no longer exists as an explicit requirement; however, the concept still underpins ISO 14001:2015 and is embodied in risk-based thinking.

Documented Information:

Required:

None

Cross-Reference 2004:

New requirement

Internal Audit Questions:	Management:
Internal auditors may ask:	Changes:
• Does the organization determine opportunities for improvement (see 9.1, 9.2, and 9.3) and implement necessary actions to achieve the intended outcomes of its EMS?	• As appropriate, improve processes to prevent nonconformities, improve products and services to meet known and predicted requirements, and improve environmental management system results.

ISO 14001:2015—Section 10.1
General

The organization shall determine and select opportunities for improvement and implement any necessary actions to meet customer requirements and enhance customer satisfaction.

Improvement shall include:

Improving products and services to meet requirements

Examples of improvement can include:

- Correction
- Corrective action
- Continual improvement
- Breakthrough change
- Innovation
- Reorganization

Correcting, preventing, or reducing undesired effects

Improving products and services to address future needs and expectations

Improving the performance and effectiveness of the environmental management system

Changes from ISO 14001:2004:

- Clause 10.1 clarifies the requirements for improvement (from old clauses 5.6, 8.3, and portions of 8.5).

- The phrase "opportunities for improvement" is mentioned in clause 9.3 (Management Review) and in this clause. This phrase, or its intent, is also added for emphasis at clauses 4.4 (Environmental Management System), and 5.3 (Organizational Roles, Responsibilities and Authorities).

- The requirements to "meet customer requirements" and "enhance customer satisfaction" are expressed in the old standard but not in old clause 8.5 (Improvement). These requirements are specifically called out in this clause.

- This clause also calls out specific requirements to address predictive requirements, such as the need to "address future needs and expectations" and in "preventing or reducing undesired effects."

The Standard: 10.0 Improvement

10.2 Nonconformity and corrective action

This clause sets out how the organization is required to act when nonconformity is identified. In such instances, the organization is required to take whatever action is necessary to control and correct the nonconformity and to deal with any resultant environmental impact. The organization should also determine if similar nonconformity has occurred elsewhere and consequently whether it needs to take similar corrective action.

In the case of an emergency, the organization should trigger the emergency plan (see 8.2). The organization also has to consider whether any further action is required to prevent a similar nonconformity recurring at the same place or occurring somewhere else, at some point in the future.

This requires the organization to determine what caused the nonconformity and then to consider whether the potential for a similar problem remains.

Documented Information:

Required:

10.2—NC/CA—PA program evidence

Cross-Reference 2004:

4.5.3 Nonconformity, corrective action and preventive action

Internal Audit Questions:	*Management:*
Internal auditors may ask:	Changes:
• When a nonconformity occurs, does the organization react to the nonconformity?	• When a nonconformity occurs, including those arising from complaints, the organization must react to the nonconformity and, as applicable, take action to control and correct it, as well as deal with the consequences.
• Does the organization, as applicable:	
a) Take action to control and correct it?	
b) Deal with the consequences, including mitigating adverse environmental impacts?	
c) Evaluate the need for action to eliminate the causes of the nonconformity, in order that it does not recur or occur elsewhere?	

ISO 14001:2015—Section 10.2
Nonconformity and corrective action

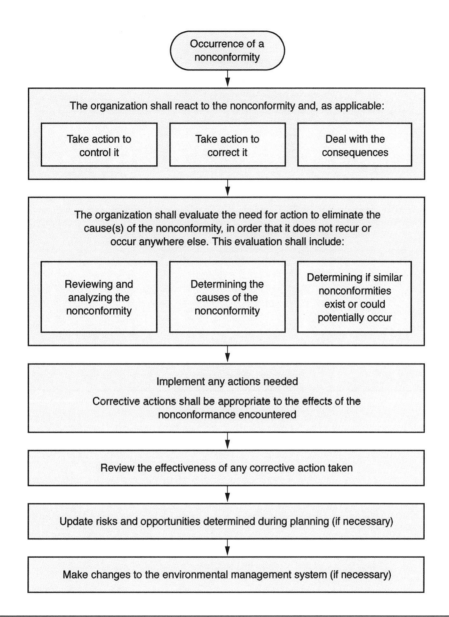

Changes from ISO 14001:2004:

- Corrective action requirements from old clause 4.5.3 are now stated in new clause 10.2.

- A documented procedure is not required.

- The new standard adds that the organization must react to a nonconformance first by controlling and correcting it, then it must take action to deal with the consequences.

- This standard adds the requirement to determine if similar nonconformances exist or could potentially occur.

- There is a new requirement to, if necessary, update risks and opportunities determined during planning.

- There is a new requirement to, if necessary, make changes to the environmental management system.

ISO 14001:2015—Section 10.2
Nonconformity and corrective action

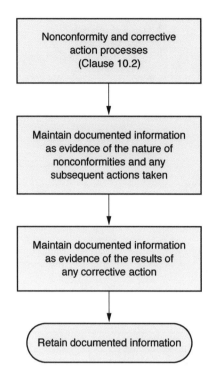

Changes from ISO 14001:2004:

• The term "documented information" in the new standard replaces the term "records" from the old standard.

• The term "nature of nonconformities" refers to the outcomes of investigative activities.

• "Any subsequent actions taken" refers to actions taken for controlling and correcting the nonconformance.

• The "results" (changes and effects) of any corrective action taken must also be documented as evidence.

The Standard: 10.0 Improvement

10.3 Continual improvement

This clause requires the organization to work continually to improve its environmental management system in terms of its suitability, adequacy, and effectiveness.

As part of the continual improvement process, the organization is specifically required to use the outputs from analysis and evaluation (see clause 9.1) and from management review (see clause 9.3) to determine areas of underperformance and to identify any opportunities for improvement.

Tools and methodologies should be employed as appropriate by the organization to investigate the cause of underperformance and to support continual improvement.

The standard provides help to interpret some terms used in this clause:

- "Continual" means that this activity occurs over a period of time, but with potential intervals of interruption, while "continuous" means duration without interruption.

- "Suitability" means how the EMS fits the organization; "adequacy" means whether it meets the requirements of ISO 14001:2015, while "effectiveness" is whether it is achieving the desired results.

Documented Information:

Required:

None

Cross-Reference 2004:

4.5.3 Nonconformity, corrective action and preventive action

Internal Audit Questions:	Management:
Internal auditors may ask: • Does the organization continually improve the suitability, adequacy, and effectiveness of the environmental management system to enhance environmental performance?	Changes: • Consider the outputs of analysis and evaluation and the outputs of management review to confirm if there are areas of underperformance or opportunities that must be addressed as part of continual improvement. • Examples: Six Sigma efforts, lean initiatives, kaizen events, kanbans in-place, Value Stream Mapping charts, TRIZ studies, Theory of Constraints teams, etc.

ISO 14001:2015—Section 10.3
Continual improvement

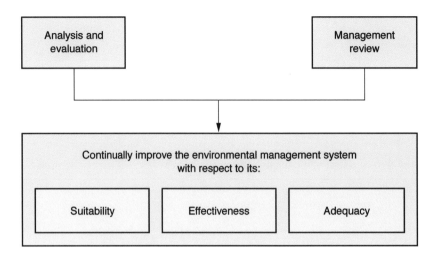

Changes from ISO 14001:2004:

• Clause 10.3 maintains the requirement for "continual improvement."

• The output from performance evaluation, "analysis and evaluation" (clause 9.1), and "management review" (clause 9.3) are drivers to identify underperformance and opportunities for continual improvement of the environment management system.

• The requirement to improve the "effectiveness" in this clause is the same as in old clause 4.5.3.

• This clause adds the requirements to improve the "suitability" and "adequacy" of the quality management system.

UPDATES TO ISO 14001:2004 IN ISO 14001:2015

(Source: L. Whittington)

10. Improvement

10.1 General

This is a new clause. Organizations should ensure that they have mechanisms in place to review the results of all evaluations carried out within the EMS, to identify opportunities for improvement, and to then take action to implement them.

Opportunities for improvement may include corrective action (see 10.2) and continual improvement (see 10.3) but also breakthrough and innovation opportunities.

In other words, organizations should not only seek to improve the EMS in incremental steps but should also try to jump to distinctly higher levels of environmental performance.

10.2 Nonconformity and Corrective Action

The common Annex SL text for this clause has been expanded by ISO 14001:2015 to react to a nonconformity with "immediate" action to control and correct it, as well as to mitigate adverse environmental impacts. It also adds that corrective actions must be appropriate to the "significance" of the effects of the nonconformity, including the environmental impact.

10.3 Continual Improvement

This clause should be seen as another example of improvement as required in clause 10.1, General.

Note that clause 10.3 requires the organization to improve its EMS, but its environmental performance can be enhanced by just applying the EMS or improving one or more of its elements.

ISO 14001:2015 clarifies that the reason for continually improving the environmental management system is to enhance environmental performance.

ISO 14001:2015

Environmental Management System—Documented Information Requirements

Clause	Title	Description
4.3	Determining the scope of the environmental management system	Scope statement
5.2	Environmental policy	Environmental policy statement
6.1.1	General	Risks and opportunities
6.1.2	Environmental aspects	Environmental aspects and impacts
6.1.3	Compliance obligations	Compliance obligations
6.2.1	Environmental objectives	Environmental objectives
7.2	Competence	Training evidence
7.4.1	General	Evidence of communication
7.5.1a,b	General (See *Note*)	Required by standards
7.5.2	Creating and updating	Document identification
7.5.3	Control of documented information	Document control
7.5.3	Control of documented information	Control process
7.5.3	Control of documented information (See *Note* x2)	External documents
8.1	Operational planning and control	Process confidence
8.2	Emergency preparedness and response	Process confidence
9.1.1	General	Monitoring evidence
9.1.2	Evaluation of compliance	Compliance evaluation
9.2.2	Internal audit program	Audit program evidence
9.3	Management review	Management review results
10.2	Nonconformity and corrective action	NC/CA nature and results

ISO 14001:2004 to ISO 14001:2015—Correlation Matrix

ISO 14001:2015		Correlation Matrix	ISO 14001:2004
Clause title	**Clause number**	**Clause number**	**Clause title**
Introduction	0	0	Introduction
Scope	1	1	Scope
Normative references	2	2	Normative references
Terms and definitions	3	3	Terms and definitions
Context of the organization (title only)	4		
		4	Environmental management system requirements (title only)
Understanding the organization and its context	4.1		
Understanding the needs and expectations of interested parties	4.2		
Determining the scope of the environmental management system	4.3	4.1	General requirements
Environmental management system	4.4	4.1	General requirements
Leadership (title only)	5		
Leadership and commitment	5.1		
Environmental policy	5.2	4.2	Environmental policy
Organizational roles, responsibilities and authorities	5.3	4.4.1	Resources, roles, responsibility and authority
Planning (title only)	6	4.3	Planning (title only)
Actions to address risks and opportunities (title only)	6.1		
General	6.1.1		
Environmental aspects	6.1.2	4.3.1	Environmental aspects
Compliance obligations	6.1.3	4.3.2	Legal and other requirements
Planning action	6.1.4		
Environmental objectives and planning to achieve them (title only)	6.2	4.3.3	Objectives, targets and program(s)
Environmental objectives	6.2.1		
Planning actions to achieve environmental objectives	6.2.2		

Continued

ISO 14001:2004 to ISO 14001:2015—Correlation Matrix *Continued*

ISO 14001:2015		Correlation Matrix	ISO 14001:2004	
Clause title	Clause number	Clause number	Clause title	
Support (title only)	7	4.4	Implementation and operation (title only)	
Resources	7.1	4.4.1	Resources, roles, responsibility and authority	
Competence	7.2	4.4.2	Competence, training and awareness	
Awareness	7.3			
Communication (title only)	7.4	4.4.3	Communication	
General	7.4.1			
Internal communication	7.4.2			
External communication	7.4.3			
Documented information (title only)	7.5	4.4.4	Documentation	
General	7.5.1			
Creating and updating	7.5.2	4.4.5	Control of documents	
		4.5.4	Control of records	
Control of documented information	7.5.3	4.4.5	Control of documents	
		4.5.4	Control of records	
Operation (title only)	8	4.4	Implementation and operation (title only)	
Operational planning and control	8.1	4.4.6	Operational control	
Emergency preparedness and response	8.2	4.4.7	Emergency preparedness and response	
Performance evaluation (title only)	9	4.5	Checking (title only)	
Monitoring, measurement, analysis and evaluation (title only)	9.1	4.5.1	Monitoring and measurement	
General	9.1.1			
Evaluation of compliance	9.1.2	4.5.2	Evaluation of compliance	
Internal audit (title only)	9.2	4.5.5	Internal audit	
General	9.2.1			
Internal audit programme	9.2.2			
Management review	9.3	4.6	Management review	

ISO 14001:2004 to ISO 14001:2015—Correlation Matrix *Continued*

ISO 14001:2015	Correlation Matrix		ISO 14001:2004
Clause title	Clause number	Clause number	Clause title
Improvement (title only)	10		
General	10.1		
Nonconformity and corrective action	10.2	4.5.3	Nonconformity, corrective action and preventive action
Continual improvement	10.3		
Guidance on the use of this international standard	Annex A	Annex A	Guidance on the use of this international standard
Correspondence between ISO 14001:2015 and ISO 14001:2004	Annex B	Annex B	Correspondence between ISO 14001:2004 and ISO 9001:2000
Bibliography			Bibliography
Alphabetical index of terms	Index		

Sources of Information

ISO 9000:2015: *Quality management systems—Fundamentals and vocabulary*

ISO 9000 provides an essential background for the proper understanding and implementation of this International Standard. The environmental management principles are described in detail in ISO 9000 and have been taken into consideration during the development of this International Standard. These principles are not requirements in themselves, but they form the foundation of the requirements specified by this International Standard. ISO 9000 also defines the terms, definitions, and concepts used in this International Standard.

ISO 14001:2015: *Environmental management systems—Requirements*

ISO 14001 (this International Standard) specifies requirements aimed primarily at giving confidence in the products and services provided by an organization and thereby enhancing customer satisfaction. Its proper implementation can also be expected to bring other organizational benefits, such as improved internal communication and better understanding and control of the organization's processes.

ISO 9004:2009: *Quality management systems—Managing for the sustained success of an organization*

ISO 9004 provides guidance for organizations that choose to progress beyond the requirements of this International Standard to address a broader range of topics that can lead to improvement of the organization's overall performance. ISO 9004 includes guidance on a self-assessment methodology for an organization to be able to evaluate the level of maturity of its environmental management system.

ISO 19011:2011: *Guidelines for auditing management systems*

ISO 19011 provides guidance on the management of an audit program, on the planning and conducting of an audit of a management system, as well as on the competence and evaluation of an auditor and an audit team. ISO 19011 is intended to apply to auditors, organizations implementing management systems, and organizations needing to conduct audits of management systems.

ISO/IEC Directives, Part 1 Consolidated ISO Supplement—*Procedures Specific to ISO (Annex SL)*

WHY ASQ?

ASQ is a global community of people passionate about quality, who use the tools, their ideas and expertise to make our world work better. ASQ: The Global Voice of Quality.

FOR INDIVIDUALS

Advance your career to the next level of excellence.

ASQ offers you access to the tools, techniques and insights that can help distinguish an ordinary career from an extraordinary one.

FOR ORGANIZATIONS

Your culture of quality begins here.

ASQ organizational membership provides the invaluable resources you need to concentrate on product, service and experiential quality and continuous improvement for powerful top-line and bottom-line results.

ASQ
The Global Voice of Quality

www.asq.org/why-asq

BELONG TO THE QUALITY COMMUNITY

JOINING THE ASQ GLOBAL QUALITY COMMUNITY GIVES YOU A STRONG COMPETITIVE ADVANTAGE.

For people passionate about improvement, ASQ is the global knowledge network that links the best ideas, tools, and experts — because ASQ has the reputation and reach to bring together the diverse quality and continuous improvement champions who are transforming our world.

- 75,000 individual and organizational members in 150 countries
- 250 sections and local member communities
- 25 forums and divisions covering industries and topics
- 30,000+ Quality Resources items, including articles, case studies, research and more
- 19 certifications
- 200+ training courses

ASQ

The Global Voice of Quality

For more information, **visit asq.org/communities-networking.**

ASQ'S ONLINE QUALITY RESOURCES IS THE PLACE TO:

- Stay on top of the latest in quality with Editor's Pick and Most Popular
- Browse topics in Learn About Quality
- Find definitions in the Quality Glossary
- Search ASQ's collection of articles, books, tools, training, and more

QUALITY RESOURCES
www.asq.org/quality-resources

Connect with ASQ staff for personalized help hunting down the knowledge you need, the networking opportunities that will keep your career and organization moving forward, and the publishing opportunities that offer the best fit for you.

www.asq.org/quality-resources

ASQ
The Global Voice of Quality

TRAINING   CERTIFICATION   CONFERENCES   MEMBERSHIP   PUBLICATIONS

ASK A LIBRARIAN

Did you know?

Quality Resource contains a wealth of knowledge and information available to ASQ members and non-members.

A librarian is available to answer research requests using ASQ's ever-expanding library of relevant, credible quality resources, including journals, conference proceedings, case studies and Quality Press publications.

ASQ members receive free internal information searches and reduced rates for article purchases.

You can also contact the Quality Information Center to request permission to reuse or reprint ASQ copyrighted material, including journal articles and book excerpts.

For more information or to submit a question, visit asq.org/quality-resources.

ASQ

The Global Voice of Quality